The link between good nutrition and appropriate
development in the early years of life has long be
research, however, has highlighted the impact of
on **lifelong wellbeing**.

**What we eat as infants can determine our food choices and
overall health for the rest of our lives.**

WHAT solids you first feed (or don't feed) your baby can increase
their risk of food allergies and chronic diseases such as diabetes,
cardiovascular disease and high blood pressure. Some studies have even
found that early food patterns can impact IQ.

HOW you introduce solids can impact your baby's habits and may lead
to fussy eating.

WHEN you first introduce solids is just as important as what and how.
Relying solely on breastmilk/formula for too long and delaying the
introduction of solids is detrimental to cognition and physical growth. It
is essential that parents understand their baby's hunger and satiety cues.
Although always undertaken with good intentions, using food to comfort
or as a reward is discouraged as this can lead to unhealthy eating habits
and overweight or obesity.

Good choices are easy to make. This book provides you with the
knowledge to confidently make these choices.

Starting Solids

Published by Turtle Publishing, 2022

ISBN: 978-0-6455646-1-7

Text & recipes © Lindsey Jude

Editor: Geraldine Thurlby

Food Photography: Gratifood

Cover & text design by Gideon Caringal

Illustrations © Gideon Caringal

CONTENTS

INTRODUCTION

What, when and how you introduce foods to your baby can impact your child's food preferences and health for the rest of their lives.

In this book the term 'complementary feeding' refers to the introduction of solid foods and liquids other than breast milk/formula. During the period of complementary feeding, babies are growing and developing very quickly which can put them at risk of nutrient deficiencies.[1]

This book has used evidence-based, best practice Australian guidelines to create a simple guide to introducing solids in a safe and enjoyable way. It is important to note that all babies are individual and, therefore, this is a guide only. This book provides tips to help your child not only enjoy eating a variety of foods but also reduce their risk of developing allergies and fussy eating.

Why do we need to introduce solids?

By 6 months, breastmilk alone is not adequate to meet all your baby's nutritional needs, in particular iron and zinc. Iron is especially important because it enables oxygen to circulate around the body and plays a role in your baby's alertness and soothability.[2] If your baby becomes iron deficient this could lead to issues with cognition, the immune system, developmental delays, motor control, social interactions, slowed weight gain, fatigue, reduced appetite and they may be more cranky or fussy.[3,4] Research indicates that infants and young children are at particular risk of iron deficiency because their rapid growth leads to high iron requirements.[5]

Additionally, research has established that once complementary feeding begins, more than 90% of a breastfed infant's iron requirements must be met by complementary foods.[6] Zinc is important for growth and the immune system. Iron and zinc can be found in meat (e.g. red meat, chicken, fish), le-gumes (e.g. chickpeas, lentils, soy), nuts and seeds. Furthermore, introducing solids is important for the development of motor skills.[7]

In addition to solids, it is encouraged that breast-feeding continues through to 12 months (and up to 2 years if happy to do so) as breastmilk remains a good source of nutrition.

When should solids be introduced?

Current research indicates that solids can safely be introduced at any time between the start of 4 months (17 weeks) to the start of 6 months (26 weeks) **but not before 4 months**.[7] However, many healthcare professionals encourage caregivers to wait until the start of 6 months of age before introducing solids for the following reasons:[7]

- babies have better head control – this is key for safe swallowing.

- babies have a tongue thrust/extrusion reflex

up until 4 – 6 months (this reflex pushes food out of the baby's mouth). If still present when introducing foods, this can cause your baby to feel unsafe.

- babies are more able to display signs of 'fullness' - this is important to prevent fussy eating

- introducing solids too early may lead to reduced breast milk supply (a result of supply and demand)

Every baby develops at different rates. If you see signs that your baby is **developmentally ready** for the introduction of solids, then go for it as the research supports you!

Signs your baby is developmentally ready for the introduction of solids:

- able to sit relatively unaided

- can pick up objects and bring to mouth

- tongue thrust reflex is gone – it is a natural response for a child to push food out of the mouth when first starting solids but if your child is continually doing this then it may indicate the tongue thrust reflex is still there

Other signs may include:

- leaning towards you/looking interested when you are eating

- chewing movements with mouth

- trying to grab food

If you see the above signs or your child has reached the age of 6 months, then get started!

NUTRITION

The foods you first provide your child affects their health, not just in the short term, but also in the long term. Did you know our food preferences actually start in the early years of life?

Australian Dietary Guidelines

The Australian dietary guide to healthy eating identifies five core food groups:[8]

- meats and alternatives
- vegetables and legumes
- fruit
- grain (cereal) foods
- milk, yoghurt, cheese and/or their alternatives

Including a variety of foods each day from all five food groups will help your child:[8,9,10,11,12]

- obtain the nutrients required for growth
- stay healthy and reduce the risk of health conditions such as asthma, lifestyle diseases such as cardiovascular disease, cancer and allergies
- establish lifelong preferences for healthier foods

Variety is key. Not only is it important to include foods from the 5 food groups, but it is essential to include a variety of foods from within each group. This is because the foods within each food group contain different nutrients. For example, in the fruits group, oranges are a great source of vitamin C, which is important for skin and immune function, while blueberries are high in compounds that may help reduce lifestyle diseases.

☺ **Fun fact**

Studies have found that children who consumed blueberries had increased cognition and improved mood.[13,14]

Each of the food groups contain a great variety of vitamins and minerals, all of which are essential for growth, repair of the body and bodily functions.

Below is an overview of the **benefits of each food group for your baby**.

Meats & Alternatives

Benefits: high in iron, zinc and protein (important for growth and repair of the body). Meat contains arachidonic acid which is important for brain development. Fish is a good source of omega 3 fatty acids (DHA) which is also important for brain development.

Meat including red meat, chicken, pork, lamb, fish, shellfish and alternatives (e.g. legumes, nuts, seeds) are great sources of iron but **not all iron is ab-**

sorbed the same way. Generally, animal foods contain iron sources that are easy for the body to absorb, whereas, plant based sources of iron (e.g. legumes, nuts and seeds) are harder for the body to absorb. Regardless of this, regular intake of plant sources of iron is very healthy and is recommended.

> ♀ Tip
>
> **To improve iron absorption**, add vitamin C containing foods to the meal. This increases the body's ability to absorb the iron in the food.[1] Foods containing vitamin C include: citrus fruit, tomato, capsicum, broccoli, cauliflower, peas, kiwi fruit, rockmelon, pineapple and berries.

As has been stated, some foods can increase iron absorption, but be aware that, additionally, **some foods can inhibit iron absorption**. Calcium rich foods (e.g. dairy products such as milk, yoghurt and cheese) and tea can reduce iron absorption.

> ♀ Tip
>
> **Limit adding calcium rich foods to iron containing foods** (e.g. don't provide yoghurt at the end of a meal as 'dessert' – you are better to keep this as a snack separate to the iron containing meal.)

> ♀ Tip
>
> **Liver should not be provided more than once a week.**[15] Although liver is a good source of iron, excess liver intake may lead to vitamin A toxicity.[8] In children, vitamin A toxicity may lead to drowsiness, irritability, vomiting, anorexia and increased intracranial pressure (pressure around the brain).[16]

Vegetables and Legumes/beans (e.g. lentils, chickpeas, tofu)

Benefits of vegetables: high in nutrients, fibre and can help with the absorption of other nutrients e.g.

vitamin C in broccoli helps iron absorption from legumes.

Benefits of legumes: great source of protein, carbohydrates (body's main energy source), fibre and iron. Examples: lentils, chickpeas, soybeans, tofu, cannellini beans, kidney beans and split peas.

Fibre: Fibre is helpful for a number of reasons. Firstly, fibre helps keep your baby's bowels healthy and moving as it bulks up the stools and absorbs water to soften stools. Some studies have found eating a high fibre diet may reduce the risk of developing food allergies,[17] asthma and wheezing.[18] Additionally, it also feeds good gut bacteria which contribute to the immune system, which protects the body against things such as bacteria, viruses and toxins.

> ♀ Tip
>
> **Include a variety of coloured vegetables throughout the week** to ensure a wide variety of nutrients are consumed. For example, orange vegetables contain vitamin A, which is important for vision and immunity.[4] Green, leafy vegetables contain folate which is important for cell growth, mood and cognition.[19]

Fruit

Benefits: nutrient dense, high in fibre and contain antioxidants which prevent cancer and chronic conditions.

> ♀ Tip
>
> **Provide fresh fruit and never fruit juice.** Juice is not the same as eating a fresh piece of fruit. During fruit juice production, many of the nutrients are destroyed and the fibre is removed leaving just concentrated sources of sugar. Excessive intake of juice has been found to lead to tooth decay, obesity, reduced appetite and gastrointestinal symptoms (such as bloating, abdominal pain and loose bowel motions).

Grain (cereal) foods

Benefits: excellent source of carbohydrates which are the body's main fuel source (like 'petrol for your engine'). However, **not all grains are the same**.

It is important to know the difference between wholegrains vs refined (highly processed) grains, as they do not have the same benefits.[20] Whenever possible, use wholegrains as they have been found to be protective against cancers, lifestyle diseases (cardiovascular disease and diabetes) as well as obesity.[21]

WHOLEGRAINS	REFINED GRAINS
The whole grain is intact.	The outer layer and germ of the grain are generally removed.

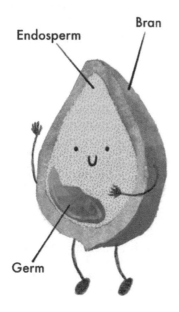

Endosperm

Bran

Germ

Endosperm

Bran contains: most nutrients, fibre, vitamins E and B's, folate, thiamin and antioxidants.

Endosperm contains: carbohydrates and protein.

Germ contains: essential fatty acids, vitamins E and B's, minerals and antioxidants.

Endosperm contains: carbohydrates and protein.

Whole grains are harder for your body to digest, which means you stay fuller for longer (low GI).

Refined grains are easy for your body to digest. This leads to sugar spikes, followed by sugar lows (high GI). (Visualise a child with a sugar high, followed by a sugar crash).

Examples of wholegrains vs refined grains are listed below

WHOLEGRAINS	REFINED GRAINS
brown rice (choose long grain as this is low GI)	white rice (particularly short grains)
wholegrain/wholemeal bread	white bread
pearl couscous	couscous
rolled oats	quick oats
wholemeal pasta	white pasta
quinoa	puffed quinoa

Other great wholegrains include: barley, millet, spelt, freekeh and buckwheat

Milk, Yoghurt, Cheese and/or Alternatives (eg fortified soy milk)

Benefits: good source of protein and calcium which is important for bone health.

Note: breastmilk or formula should be the main source of calcium in the first year of life.

> ♀ Tip
>
> **ALWAYS give babies full fat dairy products.** Children require fat for growth, therefore, it is not recommended to offer low fat varieties of food before the age of 2 years old.

Fats

Not all fats are the same. When cooking, it is recommended to use healthy (unsaturated) fats such as extra virgin olive oil.[8] These fats can have positive effects on physical and mental health and may reduce the risk of developing type 2 diabetes or cardiovascular disease.[8]

In contrast, saturated fats, such as butter and coconut oils, are not good for health and may increase the risks of chronic lifestyle diseases such as cardiovascular disease and diabetes.[8]

Good fat options for cooking and baking:

- extra virgin olive oil (use 'extra virgin' rather than 'regular' or 'light' as it has more antioxidants)

Fats that should be used less often include:

- butter
- coconut oil
- vegetable oil
- palm oil

Foods and fluids NOT suitable for infants:[7]

UNSUITABLE ITEM	REASON
Foods	
Small and/or hard foods e.g. nuts, seeds or raw, hard vegetables/fruit such as carrot, celery, apple.	Pose a choking risk and should be avoided in the first 3 years of life.
Discretionary ('sometimes') foods e.g. biscuits, cakes, chips, deep fried foods, lollies, chocolate, processed meats such as ham, sausages, bacon, frankfurts and cabanossi. ✍ **NOTE** The *Australian Dietary Guidelines* classify processed meats as discretionary foods due to the high sodium and saturated fat content and links to cancer.[23] It is therefore recommended that you should limit your family's intake of these products.	Not essential for health. Provide little nutrition (little to no vitamins, minerals, fibre) and are high in 'bad' fats, salt, sugar and calories. When eaten regularly or in large quantities this can cause weight gain and may lead to lifestyle diseases such as heart disease or type 2 diabetes. Some studies have found regular intake of discretionary foods reduces IQ scores in children.[22]
Undercooked egg or protein (e.g. fish, meat, chicken, shellfish)	May lead to food poisoning.
Honey	May contain clostridium botulinum (botulism), which can lead to serious illness and even paralysis in severe cases. Therefore, do not feed infants younger than 12 months of age any type of honey.
Low fat or reduced fat options e.g. low fat/ skim milk or cheese	Children require fat for growth and to help meet their high energy requirements, therefore, it is not recommended to offer low fat varieties of food before the age of 2 years old.
Sugar – *do not add to food*	Increases the risk of tooth decay. Our teeth have bacteria (good and bad) residing on them. Bad bacteria feed on sugar which creates acid that destroys the outer layer of the tooth (enamel). Therefore, extended exposure to sugary foods may lead to tooth decay e.g. providing fruit in a mesh feeder.

UNSUITABLE ITEM	REASON
Salt (sodium) – *do not add to food* Salt is found in many foods (particularly processed foods, but it is also found in cheese, cereal and bread). When buying foods for your child it may be helpful to look at the nutrition label. Try to choose foods lower in salt (sodium). When comparing products, always compare per 100g, as serving sizes can vary from product to product. For example, regular *Weet-Bix* has 270mg of sodium/100g whereas, Weet-Bix Kids only has 45mg of sodium/100mg.	Negatively affects kidneys and blood pressure. Babies are born with immature kidneys and therefore it may be hard for your child to excrete excess salt from the body. Additionally, salt can affect their blood pressure - both immediately and put them at risk of high blood pressure (hypertension) later in life.

Fluids

Juice	Juice is not the same as eating a fresh piece of fruit. During fruit juice production, many of the nutrients are destroyed and the fibre is removed leaving just concentrated sources of sugar. Excessive intake of juice has been found to lead to tooth decay, obesity, reduced appetite and gastrointestinal symptoms (such as bloating, abdominal pain and loose bowel motions).[24] Whole fruit is a better option.
Cow's milk or cow milk alternatives such as soy, almond, oat or rice milk (however, small amounts mixed into food is OK)	**Cow's milk** – large volumes can lead to reduced appetite and can lead to iron deficiencies as milk displaces iron rich foods and calcium prevents iron absorption. Unpasteurized milks have increased infection risks and should not be provided to your child **Cow milk alternatives** lack the appropriate nutrients required for infants' growth. **Rice milk** is not recommended for infants and young children as it contains inorganic arsenic (carcinogen).[1] Chronic intake of arsenic has been found to affect short term health, such as growth in children, as well as long term health including risk of cancer (skin, liver, lung and bladder). Arsenic intake has also been shown to lower IQ in children.[25,26,27]

UNSUITABLE ITEM	REASON
Tea, herbal teas, coffee	Studies have found tannins in caffeine based drinks may reduce absorption of iron and other nutrients.[28] **Fennel tea** and infusions are sometimes used as a treatment for infant colic. However, fennel teas (and fennel oil) contain genotoxic carcinogens and **should not be offered to children under the age of 4 years old**.[1]
Other fluids such as soft drink, energy drinks and cordial	Other fluids may impact your child's intake of breastmilk or formula. However, from 6 months, cooled, sterilized water may be offered to avoid constipation.

ALLERGIES

Allergies have been on the rise in Australia, but the rise can be stopped. **Research has found that introducing high risk allergen foods early into the diet, from around 6 months (26 weeks), but not before 4 months (17 weeks) may reduce your child's risk of developing a food allergy.**[29,30,31,32,33] This is the same for both families with a history of food allergies and families that have no such history.

The top 9 food allergies in Australia are:

- peanut
- egg
- cow's milk
- fish e.g. tuna, salmon, barramundi
- shellfish e.g. prawns
- tree nut e.g. almonds and cashews
- soy e.g. tofu, soy milk, edamame
- sesame e.g. tahini
- wheat e.g. flour, couscous, pasta, bread

It is important to note, any food may cause an allergic reaction, it is not limited to the top nine. Reactions generally occur within minutes to 2 hours, however, some reactions can be delayed. Note that mild redness around the mouth is commonly due to skin irritation rather than an allergic reaction.

Signs and Symptoms of Allergic Reaction:[33]

Stop feeding and seek medical advice if following symptoms occur:

- swelling of the lips, eyes or face
- welts or hives
- any change in your baby's behaviour e.g. unsettled
- vomiting

STOP FEEDING AND CALL AMBULANCE IMMEDIATELY if following symptoms of a severe allergic reaction (anaphylaxis) occur:

- difficulty/noisy breathing or your baby becomes pale and floppy
- tongue swelling

How to Safely Introduce Allergen Foods

Thinking around the introduction of allergen foods has changed dramatically over the last few years. It was previously thought that the best approach was to withhold allergen foods until later in life. Recent research, however, has established that this approach does not prevent food allergies and it is better to introduce allergen foods before 12 months of age (but not before 4 months (17 weeks)).

The Australasian Society of Clinical Immunology and Allergy (ASCIA) has a comprehensive website, detailing signs and symptoms and management of an allergic reaction and should be referred to prior to introducing allergenic foods: https://www.allergy.org.au.

Peanut

Egg

Cow's milk

Fish

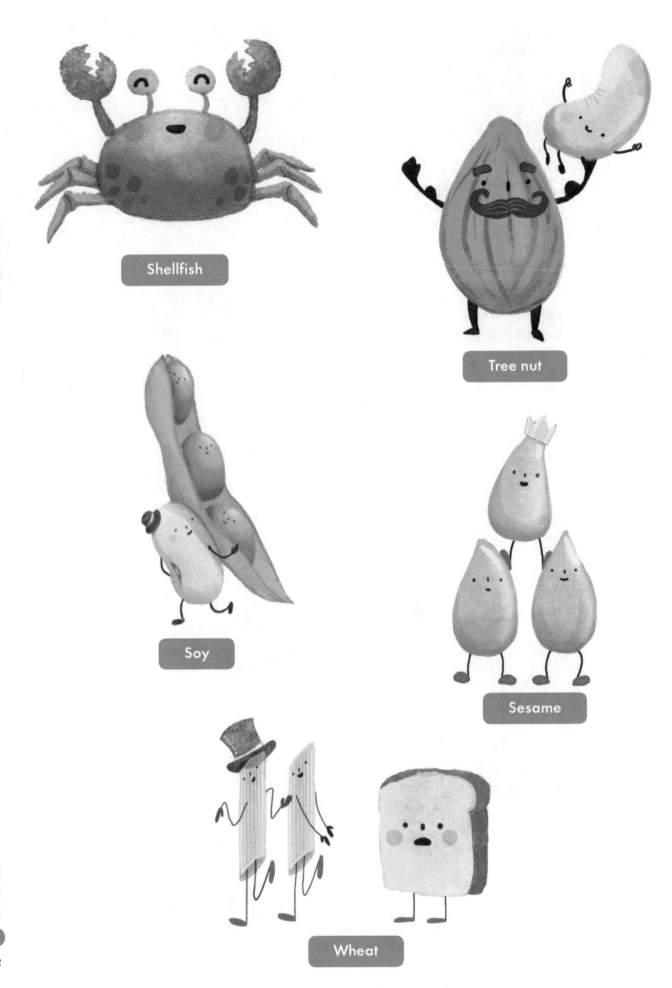

Shellfish

Tree nut

Soy

Sesame

Wheat

NOTE: If your child is at high risk of peanut allergy (e.g. has severe eczema, egg allergy, or both) it is recommended to introduce peanuts under medical supervision. For detailed information about how to introduce peanuts to children at high risk refer to
https://www.allergy.org.au.

When introducing an allergen food it is important to:[33]

- Introduce one at a time (so you know which food has caused a reaction).

- Introduce a new allergen food in the morning, so you can monitor if a reaction has occurred. NEVER introduce an allergen food at night as reactions cannot be monitored.

- Start small e.g. try ¼ teaspoon of allergen food mixed into other foods - if no reaction occurs you can increase to ½ teaspoon next time the allergen food is served. Be mindful that a reaction may not occur on the first introduction of the food but may occur after eating the food a few times. This is why it is important to slowly increase the amount every time offered.

- Offer the allergen food in appropriate textures mixed into other foods (refer 'Food Textures Progression' information in next section).

- Once introduced and no reaction has occurred, include the allergen food twice a week. Allergen foods need to be included regularly in your child's diet to help with preventing food allergies. It's not enough to just offer it every now and then. The meal plans included later in this book show how to do this.

- If you are concerned about introducing allergen foods you may rub a small amount of the allergen food on the inside of your child's lips and wait a few minutes to see if a reaction occurs. If there is no reaction, continue to offer the allergen food as recommended above.

- Do not rub or smear allergen foods on your baby's skin. This may increase the risk of your baby developing an allergy to this food.

FOOD TEXTURE PROGRESSIONS

Providing your child with appropriate food textures is important for ensuring a safe and pleasurable eating experience. Babies are not born with the ability to chew and swallow with ease. This ability develops over time and is learnt.

The Australian *Infant Feeding Guidelines* recommends a systematic, stepwise progression of textures.[7] This helps manage sensory challenges and motor skills, allowing your child to build up their eating skills safely. This also assists in meeting your baby's nutrition requirements.

The food texture progression outlined in the following pages is based on the development of oral motor skills in the average child. Note, this is just a guide. All babies are unique and some babies will move through the textures quickly and some may take more time and/or require very gradual changes to the texture. However, it is encouraged that you do not delay introducing lumpy foods after 10 months of age, as research has found this may lead to feeding difficulties and reduced intake of vegetables in mid-childhood.[34]

Minced/finely chopped

Puree

Mashed

Finger foods

Texture Progression from Introduction of Solids to 12 months of Age:[7]

AGE	TEXTURE
4–6 months	**Purees** Thin puree, with no lumps (same consistency as runny plain yogurt). When starting purees it is important that they are a thin consistency. You will require a liquid to thin out the puree and below are some options: • breastmilk* • formula* • sterilized water e.g. use cooking water used to steam vegetables • oil e.g. extra virgin olive oil *Note: Breastmilk and formula will add nutrients to the puree but it will also make the food sweet. If you want to keep the food savoury, try using healthy oils e.g. extra virgin olive oil as this will keep the food savoury but also provide energy and fat soluble vitamins.

AGE	TEXTURE
7–8 months	**Mashed** Soft foods that have been mashed or pureed with soft, small lumps **Minced/finely chopped** Roughly mashed or finely chopped (<0.5 cm in size) **Tip:** Ensure food is moist to help food hold together. If not moist, add ingredients such as hommus*, tzatziki*, yoghurt*, mashed avocado or banana. ***Note:** hommus, tzatziki and yoghurt contain allergens and should only be used once allergen has been introduced to your baby's diet and no reaction has occurred.
8–12 months	**Finger foods** Soft foods that hold together and can be picked up (approximately 4 cm × <1 cm). Foods that easily break down in the mouth with chewing. When starting finger foods, be mindful that most children under the age of 12 months are learning fine motor skills such as the pincer grip (using their finger and thumb to pick up food). To begin with, babies typically grab items with a fist grip (think of a fist full of hair being pulled). Therefore, when introducing finger foods, cut into a size and shape that is easy for your baby to pick up with a fist grip. For example, the length and half the width of your pinky finger. If providing round or spherical foods e.g. grapes or cherry tomatoes, ensure they are cut into halves or quarters to reduce choking risk. Whenever providing finger foods, always closely observe your child.

Gagging vs Choking

It is important to know the difference between gagging (loud noises, coughing) vs choking (infant is generally silent, unable to bring food up through coughing, unable to speak or cry as food is blocking the airways). Babies are born with reflexes to keep them safe such as the gag reflex which helps prevent choking. The gag reflex may occur when your baby is introduced to new foods (tastes and textures). When food moves to the back of the tongue in infants, the gag reflex may kick in and push the food back out again. But don't worry, this is a very normal and safe response. Your baby won't be upset by this unless you start becoming upset or anxious. The more you respond and react negatively, the more your baby will have a negative association with food (this may lead to fussy eating). If your child is gagging, stay positive, tell your child in a calm voice "Lets cough it up (demonstrate how to cough), *cough, cough*. There we go. All better. Good job." However, if your child continues to gag constantly and refuses most foods, bring this to the attention of your doctor and/or see a paediatric speech pathologist for an assessment.

NEVER leave a child unattended while eating. It is important to observe for signs of choking. For more information on signs of choking and choking first aid, refer to Raising Children website: https://raisingchildren.net.au/.

Choking Prevention

Posture

To prevent choking, ensure your baby is sitting in an appropriate high chair and not held by someone. Correct posture and stability will enable your baby to:

- coordinate safe chewing

- focus on the food, rather than on sitting upright

- breathe with ease

- have better hand to mouth coordination

The best position for your baby is to have their feet, knees and hip at a 90 degree angle with even weight distribution.[46]

A foot rest is essential in allowing feet, knees and hips to be at a 90 degree angle. If your child slouches, add padding or a towel to keep them upright.

Sit as close as possible to eye level with your baby (do not stand over them while feeding). If your head is above their head they will look up to maintain eye contact. This extends their head and opens up their airways leading to increased risk of choking or coughing.

Foods

It is important to provide texture appropriate foods to help prevent your child from choking. Foods that may pose a choking risk include:[7,35]

RISK FOOD	EXAMPLES	HOW TO REDUCE RISK
Hard foods	Whole nuts	Use smooth nut pastes (thinned out with sterilized water).
	Whole seeds	Use seed pastes e.g. tahini (thinned out with sterilized water).
	Hard fruits and vegetables	Cook and mash fruits and vegetables to soften (initially). As your child's eating skills develop you can reduce the cooking time and mash less and/or grate instead. Remove skin from fruit.
	Fish bones	Check for bones and remove.
	Rice cakes	Try soft bread cut into strips (4 cm × <1 cm).
	Popcorn	Avoid popcorn.
	Meat such as steak and chicken breast	Ensure meat is cooked to a soft texture (e.g. slow cook until very tender, rather than frying or grilling) and serve as per texture progression guidelines.
Round foods	Grapes, cherry tomatoes, strawberries, peas	Cut foods in halves or quarters. Ensure peas are cooked.
	Sausages	Cut into strips (approximately 4 cm × <1 cm).

Ensure you are with your child at all times when feeding. Ensure they are sitting upright and never force your child to eat. Where possible, prevent your child from putting too much food in their mouth. In case of emergency call 000.

HOW TO PREVENT FUSSY EATING

It is never the intention of parents to create fussy eaters, but it is easy to do so without realising. New parents are often fearful of starving their baby and will inadvertently adopt behaviours that lead to fussy eating.

Food Refusal

It is a natural reaction for babies to reject new flavours and textures as they are hardwired to protect themselves against any new experience which could be 'dangerous'. Infants have an innate preference for sweet and salty tastes and a dislike for bitter tastes. These preferences are an evolutionary legacy but these predispositions can be modified by the food experiences provided by parents.

Research has indicated that the earlier bitter and savoury foods are introduced into an infant's diet, the quicker these foods will be accepted by the baby. Refer to the table for the number of exposures required before new foods or flavours are accepted. Initially, food can be rejected multiple times. Remember, it is important to keep offering new foods or flavours because your baby will learn to enjoy them.[36] Remain calm and don't make a fuss if your baby rejects the food - simply remove it. The more you fuss, the more agitated your baby may become. You can be a role model by eating the same foods as your baby and showing your enjoyment.

If 'new' food is refused, don't offer a substitute favourite food. Babies will soon realise that if they refuse a food they don't like, it will be substituted with a food they do like. Don't worry, up until 9 months, most of your baby's nutritional requirements will come from breastmilk/formula. One refused meal is not going to prevent your infant from growing well.

Number of exposures required before new foods or flavours are accepted:[36,37,38,39,40,41]

Age	Exposures
0–1 years old	Very few
1–3 years old	5–10
3–4 years old	Up to 15

Tip

There's no need to provide dessert after a main meal. There is little incentive for your child to try new food or have a savoury meal if they know they will always get sweet food at the end of the meal.

Your Baby Can Regulate its Hunger

Infants are just as capable of regulating their own hunger as adults. Right from the start of complementary feeding, infants are able to adjust their food intake to match their nutritional needs for growth.[42] It is essential that you tune into your baby's hunger and satiety cues and trust that your baby can regulate their hunger and dietary intake no matter what size they are (whether they are above the 95th percentile or below the 25th percentile).

Watching out for your baby's hunger cues will help your baby have a positive eating experience, which will help reduce the risk of fussy eating.[43] **Never force feed your baby, be guided by their cues.**

Signs your baby is hungry:

- leans towards food
- appears excited when sees food
- opens mouth when food is near

Signs your baby is full:

- turns away from food
- pushes the spoon away
- closes mouth - refuses to open
- does not appear to be interested in food anymore

Appetites change from day to day. If your baby does not finish a meal, don't force them to eat. If they finish a meal and still look hungry it's OK to offer more of that meal or a healthy snack. Be accomodating and listen/tune in to your baby's needs. **Avoid using food to comfort or as a reward as this can lead to unhealthy eating habits and overweight or obesity**[1] Whilst the tradition of forcing children to finish everything on their plate before they 'get dessert' is well intentioned, the practice encourages overeating and does not allow your child to develop self regulation of hunger and satiety cues. Excessive praise for eating what might be considered 'less appealing', but healthy foods such as brussel sprouts and cabbage should be avoided as this reinforces the idea that these foods are not tasty. Additionally, studies have found that repeated encouragement and pressure of infants to eat actually has the opposite effect and infants eat less food overall.[44]

Where possible, allow your baby to feed themselves, whether it be placing the spoon in front of them to grab, or allowing them to pick up finger foods from the table. It is believed when infants take control they are better able to self regulate their own appetite.

Additionally, playing with foods allows your baby to explore the properties of the food (e.g. textures) and develop hand skills.

Food preferences are learnt. Babies are born with a preference for sweet foods and have to learn to enjoy savoury and bitter foods. **ALWAYS remember, you are responsible for *what and when* your baby eats, but it is up to your baby to decide *how much or if* they will eat.**

Routine

Routine plays a huge role in reducing fussy eating and helps your baby understand the difference between hunger and feeling full. Routine is important because:

- Constant grazing throughout the day can prevent your baby feeling real hunger. When a baby doesn't feel hungry (particularly picky eaters) they will have little motivation to work on trying new foods.

- Routines can also help your baby to feel more settled during meal time and allow them to feel confident in knowing how much they want to eat as they know when to expect the next meal. Be mindful, babies have small stomachs. They may need two or more nutritious snacks in addition to three main meals to help meet their energy and nutrient needs.

♀ Tip

Try limiting meal times to 30 mins and snack times to 15 mins - this helps your baby know there is an end to meals.

Babies are tuned in to their parents' emotions and reactions. How you react while feeding your child will affect whether your child perceives the experience to be good or bad. Remaining calm and positive will help your child to perceive the experience as good. Be mindful they may gag, make a mess (throw food on the floor) or only eat small amounts to begin with. But this is all normal as your child is learning to eat.

Sensory Preferences

Eating is a highly sensory experience involving: sight, touch, smell, taste, temperature, texture, movement and sound (e.g. the crunch of a carrot).

Every baby has different sensory preferences. Some babies may be more or less sensitive which may impact their acceptance of new foods. Remember, new food may need to be offered a few times before it is accepted. However, if your baby continues to refuse new food you may need to consider their sensory preferences.

The Hypersensitive Baby (HYPER meaning MORE)[45]

Babies who display greater sensitivity may need less sensory stimulation during meal times. They may feel easily overwhelmed by sensations and so sensory stimulation that we, as adults, consider a 'little' may feel like a 'lot' to them. They may become 'lost' in the amount of stimulus around them and forget to eat. Additionally, they may be more prone to gagging and refuse to try new foods.

Altering the environment in the following ways may help reduce stimuli and support babies that display hypersensitivity:[45]

- Create a quiet environment when eating; no loud noises or chatting.

- Ensure lighting isn't too bright.

- Have the baby sit in the same seat each meal time.

- Present food in the same way each meal time (eg: rice on the right, meat on the left).

- Use a divided plate, so food does not touch.

- Try to reduce smells e.g. curry has a strong smell, try increasing the spices slowly over time so your child adapts to this new smell.

- Have food all the same temperature or texture. Smaller increases in texture may be preferred - just enough so they can tell, but not too much so that the new texture is alarming.

- Use white or simple plate colours so that the food is the main 'star'.

The Hyposensitive Baby (HYPO meaning LESS)[45]

Babies who display less sensitivity may need more sensory stimulation during meal times. Babies who are hyposensitive may be less engaged during meal time. They lack awareness of time and thus forget to eat.

The following strategies may help babies that display hyposensitivity:[45]

- Use brightly coloured plates and/or food: appeals to sight.

- Add more textures: appeals to touch and taste.

- Talk to your baby and engage in playful facial expressions during mealtime: appeals to hearing.

- Use the food as an attention grabber by creating a game or story to gain their interest.

Be mindful that babies may be more or less sensitive to one or two senses only and not all senses. The important thing is to look out for and be aware if your baby appears to constantly refuse foods and/or only eats certain foods/textures/colours. Remember, a new food may need to be offered a few times before it is accepted. If you experience significant difficulties, seek expert advice, such as from a dietitian, speech pathologist or occupational therapist who can help with fussy eating or swallowing difficulties.

WEANING BREASTMILK/ FORMULA

In the first year of your baby's life, solid foods are meant to 'complement' your baby's diet, not replace breastmilk/formula. When solids are first introduced, your baby is developing its eating skills. Therefore, if solids replace breastmilk/formula too quickly your baby may miss out on key nutrients.

Between 4 months (17 weeks) and the end of 8 months (38 weeks) offer breastmilk/formula BEFORE solids. Your baby's main form of nutrition is still breastmilk/formula at this stage.

From the start of 9 months (39 weeks) onwards, offer solids BEFORE milk. By 9 months, most babies have developed adequate chewing and swallowing skills which enable them to consume a greater variety of foods.[47] By offering solids before breastmilk/formula you will be able to slowly increase your child's intake of solid foods and decrease the amount of breastmilk/formula they consume. If you are breastfeeding, your milk supply will slowly reduce as your child consumes less. This should be a gradual process, if you reduce breastmilk too quickly this may put you at risk of breast engorgement and/or mastitis.

♀ Troubleshooting Tips:[47]

- If your child appears disinterested in solids, try reducing breastmilk/formula. They may not be interested in food if they are full on breastmilk/formula.

- If your child is a good eater, but refusing breastmilk/formula or drinking very little, try offering breastmilk/formula less frequently, but increasing the amount per feed.

- Offer more breastmilk/formula if your child is unwell. Additionally, offering easier to chew/ favourite foods during this time will help ensure they are staying hydrated and getting adequate nutrition.

INTRODUCING SOLID FOODS

- Start with 1 iron rich meal per day, and build up to 3 meals per day by 7 months. The meal plans on the following pages demonstrate what and when to feed your baby.

- Start by introducing single foods first.

- Start with less sweet foods. Babies have preferences for sweet foods (breastmilk is sweet). Therefore, if you start by offering less sweet vegetables first, your baby will learn to enjoy these foods too.

- Try a new food every couple of days, the more variety the better.

- It is a natural tendency for parents who are spoon feeding their baby to pull the spoon against the baby's upper lip to remove food. Avoid this practice as it does not allow your baby to develop appropriate oral muscles (by learning to use their upper lip to remove food from the spoon). Instead, hold a spoon in your baby's mouth and allow your baby to learn to close their lips around the food.

- Wait until the end of a meal to clean your baby's face. Use a cloth, rather than the spoon, as using the spoon to clean your baby's face may lead to negative associations with spoons.

- Reduce distractions (e.g. no TV on in background and/or no playing with toys) as distractions make it hard for your baby to focus on the food in front of them.

Portion size

Remember, when you first begin complementary feeding, your baby is just getting used to solid food. They may only consume 1–2 teaspoons at first. As they get more comfortable with eating, the amount will increase (some infants progress quickly and some may take their time). Be led by your baby and allow them to choose how much, and if, they eat. Remember, your baby is still learning to eat solids and is getting its main form of nutrition from breastmilk/formula.

Meal Frequency

In the first year of life your baby is rapidly growing and developing. Babies stomach capacity is small, therefore to meet their high nutritional needs for growth they need to eat every 2–3 hrs.[48]

MEAL PLANS

To make your life easier, meal planning is recommended i.e. on the weekend you might plan your meals for the week, do your shopping and cook in bulk. This will save you time, money and ensure your baby is meeting their nutrient requirements. To help with meal planning, please visit eatgrowthrive.org to access a free meal planner. This meal planner is designed to make meal planning easy and ensure you include all top 9 food allergens twice weekly.

The meal plans below are based on the *Australian Infant Feeding Guidelines.*[7] It is important to note that these are just guides, every baby is unique and may need more or less of the below recommendations.

Note: If your baby was pre-term, has medical conditions or you are providing your baby a vegetarian or vegan diet it is important to seek specialist advice (e.g. from a paediatric dietitian and doctor) to ensure your baby is meeting their nutrient requirements. With supplementation, vegan diets can support normal growth and development. It is important to note, however, that failure to meet nutritional needs (e.g. vitamin B12) could lead to irreversible cognitive damage.[1]

To find a paediatric dietitian go to https://dietitiansaustralia.org.au.

Start of 4 months (17 weeks) to the start of 6 months (26 weeks)

Consistency: thin puree, with no lumps. Refer to the recipe section for puree recipes.

Frequency: one solid meal per day. Note, infants of this age should eat every 2–3 hrs.

Food: Iron containing foods such as infant cereals (rice), beef, chicken, legumes (chickpeas, lentils, butter beans), pork and lamb. It may be harder to achieve a very thin puree consistency using meat, however, it is still encouraged to include meat in your child's diet.

Note: Food Standards Australia New Zealand (FSANZ) regulates that all infant cereals need to be fortified with iron. Rice infant cereal is a great starting point as it is a source of iron and can be made into a smooth, thin puree consistency.

Additionally, rice is a low risk allergen food compared to wheat. However, the amount of iron content in different infant cereal brands can vary. An example of a rice infant cereal higher in iron is *Bellamy's Organic Baby Rice With Prebiotic 4+ Months.*

> ## ☑ IMPORTANT NOTE
> **Rice infant cereal should be limited to twice a week if possible.** Research has indicated that rice products contain levels of arsenic, which are safe for consumption, when eaten in moderation.[49]

Meal plan suggestion

	On waking (e.g. 7 am)	1 hr after waking (e.g. 8 am)	Milk feeds as needed e.g. every 2–3 hrs
	Milk Feed	Solid Breakfast	
Sunday	Breastmilk/formula	Infant rice cereal	Breastmilk/formula
Monday	Breastmilk/formula	Infant rice cereal	Breastmilk/formula
Tuesday	Breastmilk/formula	Legume puree	Breastmilk/formula
Wednesday	Breastmilk/formula	Legume puree	Breastmilk/formula
Thursday	Breastmilk/formula	Meat puree	Breastmilk/formula
Friday	Breastmilk/formula	Meat puree	Breastmilk/formula
Saturday	Breastmilk/formula	Meat puree	Breastmilk/formula

6¼ months (27 weeks)

Consistency: thin puree, with no lumps. Refer to the recipe section for puree recipes.

Frequency: 2 solid meals a day. Note, infants of this age should eat every 2–3 hrs.

Food:
Meal 1: Iron containing foods
Meal 2: Non sweet vegetables

Additional fluids: You can offer cooled, sterilized water in an open cup or sippy cup with or between meals. If you notice your child's poo becoming hard and small (pebble like) this may be a sign of constipation. Increasing boiled/sterilized, cooled water may help with constipation. If you are concerned about your child's bowel movements, speak with your healthcare professional.

Meal plan suggestion

	On waking (e.g. 7 am)	1 hr after waking (e.g. 8 am)	Milk feed (e.g. 11 am)	1 hr after milk feed (e.g. 12 pm)	Milk feeds as needed e.g. every 2–3 hrs
	Milk Feed	Solid Breakfast		Solid Lunch	
Sun	Breastmilk/ formula	Infant rice cereal	Breastmilk/ formula	Broccoli	Breastmilk/ formula
Mon	Breastmilk/ formula	Infant rice cereal	Breastmilk/ formula	Broccoli	Breastmilk/ formula
Tue	Breastmilk/ formula	Legume puree	Breastmilk/ formula	Cauliflower	Breastmilk/ formula
Wed	Breastmilk/ formula	Legume puree	Breastmilk/ formula	Cauliflower	Breastmilk/ formula
Thu	Breastmilk/ formula	Meat puree	Breastmilk/ formula	Mushroom	Breastmilk/ formula
Fri	Breastmilk/ formula	Meat puree	Breastmilk/ formula	Mushroom	Breastmilk/ formula
Sat	Breastmilk/ formula	Meat puree	Breastmilk/ formula	Beetroot	Breastmilk/ formula

6½ months (28 weeks)

Consistency: thin puree, with no lumps or, if your child is developmentally ready, slightly thicker puree with no lumps. Refer to the recipe section for puree recipes.

Tip: to make thicker purees, use less liquid when blending/pureeing foods.

Frequency: 2 solid meals per day. Note, infants of this age should eat every 2–3 hrs.

Food:
Meal 1: Iron containing foods + allergen foods
Meal 2: Non sweet vegetables

Additional fluids: You can offer cooled, sterilized water in an open cup or sippy cup with or between meals.

Allergen foods: wheat and tree nut
Wheat options:

- wheat flour (wholemeal flour is preferred as it contains more nutrients)

- wheat infant cereal

Tree nut options:

- almond meal

- hazelnut meal

- natural smooth:
  - macadamia spread
  - cashew spread
  - almond spread

How to introduce allergen foods:

- Start with only ¼ teaspoon of an allergen food **in the morning** mixed into the iron rich food. Introducing allergen foods in the morning, allows you to monitor for any reaction.

- If no reaction occurs, provide the food the next day but increase the amount to ½ teaspoon.

- Once you know the allergen food is safe to include (i.e. no reaction), include this twice a week in your child's diet.

- If your child has a reaction, do not include this food again and seek medical advice.

📅 Meal plan suggestion

	On waking (e.g. 7 am)	1 hr after waking (e.g. 8 am)	Milk feed (e.g. 11 am)	1 hr after milk feed (e.g. 12 pm)	Milk feeds as needed e.g. every 2–3 hrs
	Milk Feed	Solid Breakfast		Solid Lunch	
Sun	Breastmilk/ formula	Infant rice cereal +¼ tsp wheat flour	Breastmilk/ formula	Beetroot	Breastmilk/ formula
Mon	Breastmilk/ formula	Infant rice cereal +½ tsp wheat flour	Breastmilk/ formula	Broccoli	Breastmilk/ formula
Tue	Breastmilk/ formula	Legume puree	Breastmilk/ formula	Broccoli	Breastmilk/ formula
Wed	Breastmilk/ formula	Legume puree +¼ tsp almond meal	Breastmilk/ formula	Cauliflower	Breastmilk/ formula
Thu	Breastmilk/ formula	Meat puree +½ tsp almond meal	Breastmilk/ formula	Cauliflower	Breastmilk/ formula
Fri	Breastmilk/ formula	Meat puree	Breastmilk/ formula	Mushroom	Breastmilk/ formula
Sat	Breastmilk/ formula	Meat puree	Breastmilk/ formula	Mushroom	Breastmilk/ formula

6¾ months (29 weeks)

Consistency: slightly thicker purees, with no lumps. Refer to the recipe section for puree recipes.

Tip: to make thicker purees, use less liquid when blending/pureeing foods.

Frequency: 3 solid meals per day. Note, infants of this age should eat every 2–3 hrs.

Additional fluids: You can offer cooled, sterilized water in an open cup or sippy cup with or between meals.

Food:
Meal 1: Iron containing foods + allergen foods
Meal 2: Vegetables
Meal 3: Fresh or frozen fruit
Continue to include already tested allergen foods twice a week (if no reaction occurred) and also introduce new allergen foods.

New allergen foods: peanuts and sesame
Peanut options:

- natural smooth peanut butter (i.e. no added sugar or salt)*

Sesame options:

- smooth hulled tahini
- smooth hommus

Continue to include wheat and tree nuts twice a week in your child's diet. Note wheat has been included in the meal plan through the use of wheat infant cereal. Food Standards Australia New Zealand (FSANZ) regulates that all infant cereals need to be fortified with iron. However, the amount of iron content in different brands can vary. An example of a wheat infant cereal higher in iron is *Nestle Cerelac Oats & Wheat With Prune Infant Cereal.*

Note, do not use peanut butters that state they are roasted as roasted peanuts are more likely to trigger an allergic reaction.[50]

Meal plan suggestion

	On waking (e.g. 7 am) Milk Feed	1 hr after waking (e.g. 8 am) Solid Breakfast	Milk feed (e.g. 11 am)	1 hr after milk feed (e.g. 12 pm) Solid Lunch	Milk feed (e.g. 3 pm)	Solid feed (e.g. 5 pm) Solid Dinner	Milk feeds as needed e.g. every 2–3 hrs
Sun	Breastmilk/ formula	Infant rice cereal +¼ tsp peanut butter	Breastmilk/ formula	Beetroot	Breastmilk/ formula	Banana	Breastmilk/ formula
Mon	Breastmilk/ formula	Infant rice cereal +½ tsp peanut butter	Breastmilk/ formula	Carrot	Breastmilk/ formula	Banana	Breastmilk/ formula
Tue	Breastmilk/ formula	Infant wheat cereal	Breastmilk/ formula	Carrot	Breastmilk/ formula	Blueberries	Breastmilk/ formula
Wed	Breastmilk/ formula	Infant wheat cereal + tree nut spread	Breastmilk/ formula	Asparagus	Breastmilk/ formula	Blueberries	Breastmilk/ formula
Thu	Breastmilk/ formula	Puree meat +¼ tsp hommus	Breastmilk/ formula	Asparagus	Breastmilk/ formula	Mango	Breastmilk/ formula
Fri	Breastmilk/ formula	Puree meat +½ tsp hommus	Breastmilk/ formula	Sweet Potato	Breastmilk/ formula	Mango	Breastmilk/ formula
Sat	Breastmilk/ formula	Puree meat + tree nut spread	Breastmilk/ formula	Sweet Potato	Breastmilk/ formula	Banana	Breastmilk/ formula

7 months (30 weeks)

Note: If solids have not been introduced prior to 7 months, progress through the 27 to 29 weeks meal plans before moving onto the meal plans below.

During the first year of life your child is rapidly growing and developing. Infants' stomach capacity is small, therefore to meet their high nutritional needs for growth they need to eat every 2–3 hrs.[48] In the first months of introducing solid foods, infant meal plans can appear 'strange', as meals are very different to those of an adult. However, as solids become a greater part of an infant's food intake, meal plans begin to replicate adult meal patterns because infants can enjoy many of the same foods, with simple textural adjustments. Refer to the 'Recipes for All the Family' section of this book for simple recipes that can be used as part of meal plans.

Breakfast and Iron fortified Infant Cereal

The *Australian Dietary Guidelines* recommend 7 serves of infant cereal per week in order to meet increased iron needs in growing infants. It has been noted in research that it is difficult to meet your infant's high iron requirements without the use of iron fortified foods.[1] For this reason, the meal plans below include infant cereal at every breakfast. Food Standards Australia New Zealand (FSANZ) regulates that all infant cereals need to be fortified with iron. However, the amount of iron content in different brands can vary. An example of a wheat infant cereal higher in iron is *Nestle Cerelac Oats & Wheat With Prune Infant Cereal.*

Lunch and Dinner Must Dos

These meals should include:

- **protein foods** such as meat, fish or meat alternatives which provide protein and iron for your baby's growth.
  - Include red meat regularly. Red meat has the highest and most easily absorbed iron content.

- Fish is also a great source of Omega-3 fats which are good for brain health. According to Food Standards Australia New Zealand (FSANZ), it is safe for young children to have 2 to 3 serves (serve = 75 g) of fish per week.[51,52] The exceptions to this are deep sea perch and catfish (limit intake to one serve per week) and shark and billfish (limit intake to one serve per fortnight).

- **carbohydrates (carbs)** such as grains, cereals and starchy vegetables (e.g. sweet potato, potato, corn, peas, parsnip) as they provide your baby's main energy source.

- **vegetables** for fibre, antioxidants and nutrients.
  - Try to include at least 2 colours of vegetables each day. The more colours, the better.

Healthy Snacks

To begin with, your child may not need snacks, but as they get older (e.g. around 10 months) snacks can be helpful to achieve your child's nutrition needs. Snacks also help tie over their hunger until the next meal as infants may become cranky when too hungry. It is important to avoid food 'grazing' as this will prevent your baby from feeling true hunger. Your baby needs to learn the difference between hunger and fullness, as this will enable them to know to eat when hungry and stop when full.

Examples:

- fruit
- full fat yoghurt (no added sugar) - plain or flavoured e.g. *Rafferty's Garden No added Sugar Yoghurt*
- full fat cheese such as cottage or ricotta
- baked slices using ground nuts (refer to the recipe section for examples)

Food consistency: Soft foods that have been mashed or pureed with soft, small lumps.

Food frequency: 3 solid meals per day. Note, infants of this age should eat every 2–3 hrs. Refer to the 'Recipes for all the Family' section for meal ideas.

Additional fluids: You can offer cooled, sterilized water in an open cup or sippy cup with or between meals. If you notice your child's poo becoming hard and small (pebble like) this may be a sign of constipation. Increasing boiled/sterilized, cooled water may help with constipation. If you are concerned about your child's bowel movements, speak with your healthcare professional.

Food:
Meal 1: Infant cereal + allergen foods
Meal 2: Protein + carbohydrate + 2–3 vegetables + allergen foods
Meal 3: protein + carbohydrate + 2–3 vegetables
Continue to include already tested allergen foods twice a week (if no reaction occurred) and also introduce new allergen foods.

New allergen foods: cow's milk + egg (hard boiled)
Cow's milk options:

- full fat cow's milk
- full fat plain yoghurt
- full fat smooth ricotta

Egg:

- Both the yolk and white are suitable for your baby, however, the yolk is easier to mix with other foods

Continue to include wheat, tree nuts, peanuts and sesame twice a week in your child's diet.

Meal plan next page

Meal plan suggestion

*Note: **Fruit** can be added to breakfast cereals for variety and texture. Additionally, if your baby eats all of their lunch or dinner and still appears hungry, offer more of the savoury meal and/or fruit.

	On waking (e.g. 7 am)	1 hr after waking (e.g. 8 am)	Milk feed (e.g. 11 am)	1 hr after milk feed (e.g. 12 pm)	Milk feed (e.g. 3 pm)	Solid feed (e.g. 5 pm)	Milk feeds as needed
	Milk Feed	Solid Breakfast		Solid Lunch		Solid Dinner	
Sun	Breastmilk/ formula	Infant wheat cereal + ¼ tsp cow's milk	Breastmilk/ formula	Protein + carbs + 2–3 veg	Breastmilk/ formula	Protein + carbs + 2–3 veg	Breastmilk/ formula
Mon	Breastmilk/ formula	Infant wheat cereal + ½ tsp cow's milk	Breastmilk/ formula	Protein + carbs + 2–3 veg	Breastmilk/ formula	Protein + carbs + 2–3 veg	Breastmilk/ formula
Tue	Breastmilk/ formula	Infant wheat cereal + peanut butter	Breastmilk/ formula	Protein + carbs + 2–3 veg + hommus	Breastmilk/ formula	Protein + carbs + 2–3 veg	Breastmilk/ formula
Wed	Breastmilk/ formula	Infant wheat cereal + tree nut spread	Breastmilk/ formula	Protein + carbs + 2–3 veg	Breastmilk/ formula	Protein + carbs + 2–3 veg	Breastmilk/ formula
Thu	Breastmilk/ formula	Infant wheat cereal + ¼ tsp mashed hard boiled egg	Breastmilk/ formula	Protein + carbs + 2–3 veg	Breastmilk/ formula	Protein + carbs + 2–3 veg	Breastmilk/ formula
Fri	Breastmilk/ formula	Infant wheat cereal + ½ tsp mashed hard boiled egg	Breastmilk/ formula	Protein + carbs + 2–3 veg	Breastmilk/ formula	Protein + carbs + 2–3 veg	Breastmilk/ formula
Sat	Breastmilk/ formula	Infant wheat cereal + tree nut spread & peanut butter	Breastmilk/ formula	Protein + carbs + 2–3 veg + hommus	Breastmilk/ formula	Protein + carbs + 2–3 veg	Breastmilk/ formula

7¼ months (31 – 32 weeks)

Consistency: Soft foods that have been mashed or pureed with soft, small lumps. Refer to the recipe section for meal ideas.

Frequency: 3 solid meals per day. Note, infants of this age should eat every 2–3 hrs.

Additional fluids: You can offer cooled, sterilized water in an open cup or sippy cup with or between meals.

Food:
Meal 1: Infant cereal + allergen foods
Meal 2: Protein + carbohydrate + 2–3 vegetables + allergen foods
Meal 3: protein + carbohydrate + 2–3 vegetables
Continue to include already tested allergen foods twice a week (if no reaction occurred) and also introduce new allergen foods.

New allergen foods: soy and fish
Soy options:

- silken tofu
- full fat soy milk

Fish options

- mashed tuna or salmon - either tinned or freshly cooked

Continue to include wheat, tree nuts, peanuts, sesame, cow's milk and egg twice a week in your child's diet.

Meal plan suggestion

*Note: **Fruit** can be added to breakfast cereals for variety and texture. Additionally, if your baby eats all of their lunch or dinner and still appears hungry, offer more of the savoury meal and/or fruit.

	On waking (e.g. 7 am)	1 hr after waking (e.g. 8 am)	Milk feed (e.g. 11 am)	1 hr after milk feed (e.g. 12 pm)	Milk feed (e.g. 3 pm)	Solid feed (e.g. 5 pm)	Milk feeds as needed
	Milk Feed	Solid Breakfast		Solid Lunch		Solid Dinner	
Sun	Breastmilk/ formula	Infant wheat cereal + yoghurt	Breastmilk/ formula	Protein + carbs + 2–3 veg	Breastmilk/ formula	Protein + carbs + 2–3 veg	Breastmilk/ formula
Mon	Breastmilk/ formula	Infant wheat cereal + cow's milk + ¼ tsp silken tofu	Breastmilk/ formula	Protein + carbs + 2–3 veg	Breastmilk/ formula	Protein + carbs + 2–3 veg	Breastmilk/ formula
Tue	Breastmilk/ formula	Infant wheat cereal + ½ tsp silken tofu	Breastmilk/ formula	Protein + carbs + 2–3 veg + hommus	Breastmilk/ formula	Protein + carbs + 2–3 veg	Breastmilk/ formula
Wed	Breastmilk/ formula	Infant wheat cereal + tree nut spread & peanut butter	Breastmilk/ formula	Egg + carbs + 2–3 veg	Breastmilk/ formula	Protein + carbs + 2–3 veg	Breastmilk/ formula
Thu	Breastmilk/ formula	Infant wheat cereal + ¼ tsp fish	Breastmilk/ formula	Egg + carbs + 2–3 veg	Breastmilk/ formula	Protein + carbs + 2–3 veg	Breastmilk/ formula
Fri	Breastmilk/ formula	Infant wheat cereal + ½ tsp fish	Breastmilk/ formula	Protein + carbs + 2–3 veg	Breastmilk/ formula	Protein + carbs + 2–3 veg	Breastmilk/ formula
Sat	Breastmilk/ formula	Infant wheat cereal + tree nut spread & peanut butter	Breastmilk/ formula	Protein + carbs + 2–3 veg + hommus	Breastmilk/ formula	Protein + carbs + 2–3 veg	Breastmilk/ formula

7½ months (33 weeks)

Consistency: Roughly mashed or finely chopped (<0.5 cm in size).

Tip: ensure food is moist to help food hold together. If not moist, add ingredients such as hommus*, tzatziki*, yoghurt*, mashed avocado or banana. Note, meals in the recipe section of this book have intentionally included moistening agents to ensure correct consistency is achieved.

*Note: hommus, tzatziki and yoghurt contain allergens and should only be used once allergen has been introduced to your baby's diet and no reaction has occurred.

Frequency: 3 solid meals per day. Note infants of this age should eat every 2–3 hrs.

Additional fluids: You can offer cooled, sterilized water in an open cup or sippy cup with or between meals.

Food:
Meal 1: Infant cereal + allergen foods
Meal 2: Protein + carbohydrate + 2–3 vegetables + allergen foods
Meal 3: Protein + carbohydrate + 2–3 vegetables
Continue to include already tested allergen foods twice a week (if no reaction occurred) and also introduce new allergen foods.

New allergen foods: shellfish
Shellfish options:

- prawns, steamed & minced
- scallops, steamed & minced
- minced crab meat - either tinned or fresh steamed & minced

Continue to include wheat, tree nuts, peanuts, sesame, cow's milk, egg, soy and fish twice a week in your child's diet.

Meal plan suggestion

*Note: **Fruit** can be added to breakfast cereals for variety and texture. Additionally, if your baby eats all of their lunch or dinner and still appears hungry, offer more of the savoury meal and/or fruit.

	On waking (e.g. 7 am)	1 hr after waking (e.g. 8 am)	Milk feed (e.g. 11 am)	1 hr after milk feed (e.g. 12 pm)	Milk feed (e.g. 3 pm)	Solid feed (e.g. 5 pm)	Milk feeds as needed
	Milk Feed	Solid Breakfast		Solid Lunch		Solid Dinner	
Sun	Breastmilk/ formula	Infant wheat cereal + cow's milk	Breastmilk/ formula	Fish + carbs + 2–3 veg	Breastmilk/ formula	Protein + carbs + 2–3 veg	Breastmilk/ formula
Mon	Breastmilk/ formula	Infant wheat cereal + yoghurt	Breastmilk/ formula	Protein + carbs + 2–3 veg + soy & sesame hommus*	Breastmilk/ formula	Protein + carbs + 2–3 veg	Breastmilk/ formula
Tue	Breastmilk/ formula	Infant wheat cereal + peanut butter	Breastmilk/ formula	Protein + carbs + 2–3 veg + soy & sesame hommus*	Breastmilk/ formula	Protein + carbs + 2–3 veg	Breastmilk/ formula
Wed	Breastmilk/ formula	Infant wheat cereal + tree nut spread	Breastmilk/ formula	Egg + carbs + 2–3 veg	Breastmilk/ formula	Protein + carbs + 2–3 veg	Breastmilk/ formula
Thu	Breastmilk/ formula	Infant wheat cereal + ¼ tsp shellfish	Breastmilk/ formula	Egg + carbs + 2–3 veg	Breastmilk/ formula	Protein + carbs + 2–3 veg	Breastmilk/ formula
Fri	Breastmilk/ formula	Infant wheat cereal + ½ tsp shellfish	Breastmilk/ formula	Fish + carbs + 2–3 veg	Breastmilk/ formula	Protein + carbs + 2–3 veg	Breastmilk/ formula
Sat	Breastmilk/ formula	Infant wheat cereal + tree nut spread & peanut butter	Breastmilk/ formula	Protein + carbs + 2–3 veg	Breastmilk/ formula	Protein + carbs + 2–3 veg	Breastmilk/ formula

*Refer to page 63 for soy & sesame hommus recipe.

7¾ months (34 weeks)

Consistency: Roughly mashed or finely chopped (<0.5 cm in size).

Tip: ensure food is moist to help food hold together. If not moist, add ingredients such as hommus*, tzatziki*, yoghurt*, mashed avocado or banana. Note, meals in the recipe section of this book have intentionally included moistening agents to ensure correct consistency is achieved.

*__Note:__ hommus, tzatziki and yoghurt contain allergens and should only be used once allergen has been introduced to your baby's diet and no reaction has occurred.

Frequency: 3 solid meals per day. Note, infants of this age should eat every 2–3 hrs.

Additional fluids: You can offer cooled, sterilized water in an open cup or sippy cup with or between meals.

Food:
Meal 1: Infant cereal + allergen foods
Meal 2: Protein + carbohydrate + 2–3 vegetables + allergen foods
Meal 3: Protein + carbohydrate + 2–3 vegetables
Continue to include already tested allergen foods twice a week (if no reaction occurred).

Meal plan suggestion

*Note: **Fruit** can be added to breakfast cereals for variety and texture. Additionally, if your baby eats all of their lunch or dinner and still appears hungry, offer more of the savoury meal and/or fruit.

	On waking (e.g. 7 am)	1 hr after waking (e.g. 8 am)	Milk feed (e.g. 11 am)	1 hr after milk feed (e.g. 12 pm)	Milk feed (e.g. 3 pm)	Solid feed (e.g. 5 pm)	Milk feeds as needed
	Milk Feed	Solid Breakfast		Solid Lunch		Solid Dinner	
Sun	Breastmilk/ formula	Infant wheat cereal + cow's milk	Breastmilk/ formula	Fish + shellfish + carbs + 2–3 veg	Breastmilk/ formula	Protein + carbs + 2–3 veg	Breastmilk/ formula
Mon	Breastmilk/ formula	Infant wheat cereal + yoghurt	Breastmilk/ formula	Protein + carbs + 2–3 veg	Breastmilk/ formula	Protein + carbs + 2–3 veg	Breastmilk/ formula
Tue	Breastmilk/ formula	Infant wheat cereal	Breastmilk/ formula	Protein + carbs + 2–3 veg + soy & sesame hommus*	Breastmilk/ formula	Protein + carbs + 2–3 veg	Breastmilk/ formula
Wed	Breastmilk/ formula	Infant wheat cereal + tree nut spread	Breastmilk/ formula	Egg + carbs + 2–3 veg	Breastmilk/ formula	Protein + carbs + 2–3 veg	Breastmilk/ formula
Thu	Breastmilk/ formula	Infant wheat cereal + tree nut spread	Breastmilk/ formula	Egg + carbs + 2–3 veg	Breastmilk/ formula	Protein + carbs + 2–3 veg	Breastmilk/ formula
Fri	Breastmilk/ formula	Infant wheat cereal + peanut butter	Breastmilk/ formula	Fish + shellfish + carbs + 2–3 veg	Breastmilk/ formula	Protein + carbs + 2–3 veg	Breastmilk/ formula
Sat	Breastmilk/ formula	Infant wheat cereal + peanut butter	Breastmilk/ formula	Protein + carbs + 2–3 veg + soy & sesame hommus*	Breastmilk/ formula	Protein + carbs + 2–3 veg	Breastmilk/ formula

*Refer to page 63 for soy & sesame hommus recipe.

8–8¾ months

||||||||||||||||||||||||||||||||||||||||||||||||||||||||||||||||||||||||||||||||||||||||||||||||||||||||||

Consistency: Soft finger foods that hold together and can be picked up (approximately 4 cm × <1 cm). Foods that easily break down in the mouth with chewing.

Note: be led by your child, if they show signs they are not developmentally ready for soft finger foods, continue to offer finely chopped foods until developmentally ready. Refer to the recipe section for meal ideas.

Frequency: 3 solid meals per day. Note, infants of this age should eat every 2–3 hrs.

Additional fluids: You can offer cooled, sterilized water in an open cup or sippy cup with or between meals.

Food:
Meal 1: Infant cereal + allergen foods
Meal 2: Protein + carbohydrate + 2–3 vegetables + allergen foods
Meal 3: Protein + carbohydrate + 2–3 vegetables
Continue to include already tested allergen foods twice a week (if no reaction occurred).

MEAL PLANS 8–8¾ MONTHS

42

Meal plan suggestion

*Note: **Fruit** can be added to breakfast cereals for variety and texture. Additionally, if your baby eats all of their lunch or dinner and still appears hungry, offer more of the savoury meal and/or fruit.

	On waking (e.g. 7 am)	1 hr after waking (e.g. 8 am)	Milk feed (e.g. 11 am)	1 hr after milk feed (e.g. 12 pm)	Milk feed (e.g. 3 pm)	Solid feed (e.g. 5 pm)	Milk feeds as needed
	Milk Feed	Solid Breakfast		Solid Lunch		Solid Dinner	
Sun	Breastmilk/ formula	Infant wheat cereal + cow's milk	Breastmilk/ formula	Fish + shellfish + carbs + 2–3 veg	Breastmilk/ formula	Protein + carbs + 2–3 veg	Breastmilk/ formula
Mon	Breastmilk/ formula	Infant wheat cereal + yoghurt	Breastmilk/ formula	Protein + carbs + 2–3 veg	Breastmilk/ formula	Protein + carbs + 2–3 veg	Breastmilk/ formula
Tue	Breastmilk/ formula	Infant wheat cereal	Breastmilk/ formula	Protein + carbs + 2–3 veg + soy & sesame hommus*	Breastmilk/ formula	Protein + carbs + 2–3 veg	Breastmilk/ formula
Wed	Breastmilk/ formula	Infant wheat cereal + tree nut spread	Breastmilk/ formula	Egg + carbs + 2–3 veg	Breastmilk/ formula	Protein + carbs + 2–3 veg	Breastmilk/ formula
Thu	Breastmilk/ formula	Infant wheat cereal + tree nut spread	Breastmilk/ formula	Egg + carbs + 2–3 veg	Breastmilk/ formula	Protein + carbs + 2–3 veg	Breastmilk/ formula
Fri	Breastmilk/ formula	Infant wheat cereal + peanut butter	Breastmilk/ formula	Fish + shellfish + carbs + 2–3 veg	Breastmilk/ formula	Protein + carbs + 2–3 veg	Breastmilk/ formula
Sat	Breastmilk/ formula	Infant wheat cereal + peanut butter	Breastmilk/ formula	Protein + carbs + 2–3 veg + soy & sesame hommus*	Breastmilk/ formula	Protein + carbs + 2–3 veg	Breastmilk/ formula

*Refer to page 63 for soy & sesame hommus recipe.

9–9¾ months

SIGNIFICANT CHANGE!

Offer solids BEFORE breastmilk/formula. By 9 months, most infants have developed adequate chewing and swallowing skills which enable them to consume a greater variety of foods.[47] By offering solids **before** breastmilk/formula you will be able to slowly increase your baby's intake of solid foods and decrease the amount of breastmilk/formula they consume. If you are breastfeeding, your milk supply will slowly reduce as your child consumes less. This should be a gradual process, if you reduce breastmilk too quickly this may put you at risk of breast engorgement and/or mastitis.

Food Consistency: Soft foods that hold together and can be picked up (approximately 4 cm × <1 cm). Foods that easily break down in the mouth with chewing. Refer to the recipe section for meal ideas.

Frequency: 3 solid meals per day. Note, infants of this age should eat every 2–3 hrs.

Additional fluids: You can offer cooled, sterilized water in an open cup or sippy cup with or between meals.

Food:
Meal 1: Infant cereal + allergen foods
Meal 2: Protein + carbohydrate + 2–3 vegetables + allergen foods
Meal 3: Protein + carbohydrate + 2–3 vegetables
Continue to include already tested allergen foods twice a week (if no reaction occurred).

Meal plan suggestion

*Note: **Fruit** can be added to breakfast cereals for variety and texture. Additionally, if your baby eats all of their lunch or dinner and still appears hungry, offer more of the savoury meal and/or fruit.

	On waking (e.g. 7 am) Solid Breakfast	Milk feed 1.5 hr after waking (e.g. 8:30 am)	Solid feed (e.g. 11:30 am) Solid Lunch	Milk feed 1.5 hr after solid feed (e.g. 1 pm)	Milk feed (e.g. 3 pm)	Solid feed (e.g. 5 pm) Solid Dinner	Milk feeds as needed
Sun	Infant wheat cereal + cow's milk	Breastmilk/ formula	Fish + shellfish + carbs + 2–3 veg	Breastmilk/ formula	Breastmilk/ formula	Protein + carbs + 2–3 veg	Breastmilk/ formula
Mon	Infant wheat cereal + yoghurt	Breastmilk/ formula	Protein + carbs + 2–3 veg	Breastmilk/ formula	Breastmilk/ formula	Protein + carbs + 2–3 veg	Breastmilk/ formula
Tue	Infant wheat cereal	Breastmilk/ formula	Protein + carbs + 2–3 veg + soy & sesame hommus*	Breastmilk/ formula	Breastmilk/ formula	Protein + carbs + 2–3 veg	Breastmilk/ formula
Wed	Infant wheat cereal + tree nut spread	Breastmilk/ formula	Egg + carbs + 2–3 veg	Breastmilk/ formula	Breastmilk/ formula	Protein + carbs + 2–3 veg	Breastmilk/ formula
Thu	Infant wheat cereal + tree nut spread	Breastmilk/ formula	Egg + carbs + 2–3 veg	Breastmilk/ formula	Breastmilk/ formula	Protein + carbs + 2–3 veg	Breastmilk/ formula
Fri	Infant wheat cereal + peanut butter	Breastmilk/ formula	Fish + shellfish + carbs + 2–3 veg	Breastmilk/ formula	Breastmilk/ formula	Protein + carbs + 2–3 veg	Breastmilk/ formula
Sat	Infant wheat cereal + peanut butter	Breastmilk/ formula	Protein + carbs + 2–3 veg + soy & sesame hommus*	Breastmilk/ formula	Breastmilk/ formula	Protein + carbs + 2–3 veg	Breastmilk/ formula

*Refer to page 63 for soy & sesame hommus recipe.

10–10¾ months

Breastmilk/formula: offer solids BEFORE breast-milk/formula.

Food Consistency: Soft foods that hold together and can be picked up (approximately 4 cm × <1 cm). Foods that easily break down in the mouth with chewing. Refer to the recipe section for meal ideas.

Frequency: 3 solid meals **+ 1 healthy snack per day**. Note, infants of this age should eat every 2–3 hrs.

Additional fluids: You can offer cooled, sterilized water in an open cup or sippy cup with or between meals.

Food:
Meal 1: Infant cereal + allergen foods
Meal 2: Protein + carbohydrate + 2–3 vegetables + allergen foods
Meal 3: Protein + carbohydrate + 2–3 vegetables
Snack 1: fruit, full fat plain or flavoured yoghurt, full fat cheese such as cottage or ricotta, baked slice made with ground nuts.

Continue to include already tested allergen foods twice a week (if no reaction occurred).

Meal plan suggestion

*Note: **Fruit** can be added to breakfast cereals for variety and texture. Additionally, if your baby eats all of their lunch or dinner and still appears hungry, offer more of the savoury meal and/or fruit.

	On waking (e.g. 7 am) Solid Breakfast	Milk feed 1.5 hr after waking (e.g. 8:30 am)	Solid feed (e.g. 11:30 am) Solid Lunch	Milk feed 1.5 hr after solid feed (e.g. 1 pm)	Solid feed (e.g. 3 pm) Solid Snack	Solid feed (e.g. 5:30 pm) Solid Dinner	Milk feeds as needed
Sun	Infant wheat cereal	Breastmilk/ formula	Fish + shellfish + carbs + 2–3 veg	Breastmilk/ formula	Fruit	Protein + carbs + 2–3 veg	Breastmilk/ formula
Mon	Infant wheat cereal	Breastmilk/ formula	Protein + carbs + 2–3 veg	Breastmilk/ formula	Full fat yoghurt	Protein + carbs + 2–3 veg	Breastmilk/ formula
Tue	Infant wheat cereal	Breastmilk/ formula	Protein + carbs + 2–3 veg + soy & sesame hommus*	Breastmilk/ formula	Fruit	Protein + carbs + 2–3 veg	Breastmilk/ formula
Wed	Infant wheat cereal + tree nut spread	Breastmilk/ formula	Egg + carbs + 2–3 veg	Breastmilk/ formula	Full fat yoghurt	Protein + carbs + 2–3 veg	Breastmilk/ formula
Thu	Infant wheat cereal + tree nut spread	Breastmilk/ formula	Egg + carbs + 2–3 veg	Breastmilk/ formula	Full fat ricotta with cinnamon	Protein + carbs + 2–3 veg	Breastmilk/ formula
Fri	Infant wheat cereal + peanut butter	Breastmilk/ formula	Fish + shellfish + carbs + 2–3 veg	Breastmilk/ formula	Fruit	Protein + carbs + 2–3 veg	Breastmilk/ formula
Sat	Infant wheat cereal + peanut butter	Breastmilk/ formula	Protein + carbs + 2–3 veg + soy & sesame hommus*	Breastmilk/ formula	Baked slice made with ground nuts	Protein + carbs + 2–3 veg	Breastmilk/ formula

*Refer to page 63 for soy & sesame hommus recipe.

11 – 11¾ months

Breastmilk/formula: offer solids BEFORE breast-milk/formula.

Food Consistency: Soft foods that hold together and can be picked up (approximately 4 cm × <1 cm). Foods that easily break down in the mouth with chewing. Refer to the recipe section for meal ideas.

Frequency: 3 solid meals **+ 2 snacks** per day. Note, infants of this age should eat every 2–3 hrs.

Additional fluids: You can offer cooled, sterilized water in an open cup or sippy cup with or between meals.

Food:

Meal 1: Infant cereal + allergen foods

Meal 2: Protein + carbohydrate + 2–3 vegetables + allergen foods

Meal 3: Protein + carbohydrate + 2–3 vegetables

Snack 1 & 2: fruit, full fat plain or flavoured yoghurt, full fat cheese such as cottage or ricotta, baked slice made with ground nuts.

Continue to include already tested allergen foods twice a week (if no reaction occurred).

Meal plan suggestion

*Note: **Fruit** can be added to breakfast cereals and/or full fat yoghurt (snack 1) for variety and texture. Additionally, if your baby eats all of their lunch or dinner and still appears hungry, offer more of the savoury meal and/or fruit.

	On waking (e.g. 7 am) Solid Breakfast	2 hr after waking (e.g. 9 am) Solid Snack	Solid feed (e.g. 12 pm) Solid Lunch	Milk feed (e.g. 1:30 pm)	Solid feed (e.g. 3:30 pm) Solid Snack	Solid feed (e.g. 5:30–6:00 pm) Solid Dinner	Milk feeds as needed
Sun	Infant wheat cereal	Full fat yoghurt	Fish + shellfish + carbs + 2–3 veg	Breastmilk/formula	Fruit	Protein + carbs + 2–3 veg	Breastmilk/formula
Mon	Infant wheat cereal	Full fat yoghurt	Protein + carbs + 2–3 veg	Breastmilk/formula	Baked slice made with ground nuts	Protein + carbs + 2–3 veg	Breastmilk/formula
Tue	Infant wheat cereal	Full fat yoghurt	Protein + carbs + 2–3 veg + soy & sesame hommus*	Breastmilk/formula	Fruit	Protein + carbs + 2–3 veg	Breastmilk/formula
Wed	Infant wheat cereal	Full fat yoghurt	Egg + carbs + 2–3 veg	Breastmilk/formula	Baked slice made with ground nuts	Protein + carbs + 2–3 veg	Breastmilk/formula
Thu	Infant wheat cereal	Full fat yoghurt	Egg + carbs + 2–3 veg	Breastmilk/formula	Full fat ricotta with cinnamon	Protein + carbs + 2–3 veg	Breastmilk/formula
Fri	Infant wheat cereal + peanut butter	Full fat yoghurt	Fish + shellfish + carbs + 2–3 veg	Breastmilk/formula	Fruit	Protein + carbs + 2–3 veg	Breastmilk/formula
Sat	Infant wheat cereal + peanut butter	Full fat yoghurt	Protein + carbs + 2–3 veg + soy & sesame hommus*	Breastmilk/formula	Baked slice made with ground nuts	Protein + carbs + 2–3 veg	Breastmilk/formula

*Refer to page 63 for soy & sesame hommus recipe.

12 months

Congratulations! You have successfully navigated what can be an overwhelming period in the life of your baby. Thanks to you, your child has had the best possible start.

For recommended toddler dietary patterns you may wish to refer to the Australian Dietary Guidelines Educator Guide found at the eatforheallth.gov.au website.

FOOD SAFETY

Your child was born with a weak immune system and therefore is at higher risk of food poisoning.

Below are ways to reduce this risk:

Preparing food

- Always wash hands with soap before preparing food or feeding your child.
- Clean bench surfaces before and after preparation.
- Wash fruit and vegetables before use.

Storing food

- Store any excess food in the fridge or freezer.
- Label food with the date it was made.
- Don't let food cool down on the bench - place immediately into the fridge or freezer.
- Store prepared food in the fridge no longer than 2 days or in the freezer for up to 30 days.

Reheating

- Thaw food in the fridge, never thaw on the benchtop at room temperature. Alternatively, defrost in the microwave.
- When reheating food, heat to steaming. Stir to remove hot spots with a clean spoon and allow to cool slightly. Check that temperature is safe for consumption by putting small amounts of food against your lips.
- Wash your and your baby's hands before offering food.
- Throw away any uneaten, offered food.

RECIPES

The recipes that follow are focused on providing healthy meals that meet your baby's dietary requirements in their first year of life. Importantly, the recipes have been tested on the most demanding of audiences – my family. Every recipe was trialled on my infant son and my husband. Each recipe was adapted until it received a seal of approval from both. My son didn't need words to convey his reaction to each recipe! These recipes have been developed with love. I hope you enjoy sharing them with your family as much as I loved creating them.

Start of 4 months to end of 6 months

Tip: Cook and puree foods in batches once a week and freeze in small containers to minimise the need for daily cooking.

Meat puree (iron rich)

Meat, particularly red meat, is a great source of iron. Although it is recommended to initially offer single foods, meat can have a very grainy texture once blended. Adding cooked vegetables when blending meat helps create a smoother consistency and also increases iron absorption due to the vitamin C content of the vegetables.

Ingredients

1 tbsp extra virgin olive oil

500g mince meat (e.g. beef, lamb, veal, pork OR chicken)

1 large carrot (or 2 small), peeled and grated

2 tomatoes, skin removed and finely chopped

½ **cup** sterilized water

1 cup of extra liquid e.g. sterilized water, formula, breastmilk

Method

1. Heat oil in frying pan over med-high heat.

2. Add mince and cook for 5 mins, or until cooked through.

3. Add vegetables and water, reduce heat and simmer for 10–12 mins, or until vegetables have softened.

4. Remove from heat.

5. Transfer meat mixture and extra liquid to blender/food processor, and puree to a smooth, thin consistency, adding extra liquid as required.

Start of 4 months to end of 6 months

Tip: Cook and puree foods in batches once a week and freeze in small containers to minimise the need for daily cooking.

Legume puree (iron rich)

Legumes are a good source of iron, protein and fibre. However, plant based sources of iron are harder for the body to absorb. It is therefore recommended to add foods containing vitamin C, such as lemon juice, into the puree to enhance iron absorption.

Ingredients

1 tbsp extra virgin olive oil

420g tin no added salt cannellini OR butter beans, drained and rinsed

⅓ cup liquid e.g sterilized water, breastmilk OR formula

juice of 1 large lemon

Method

1. Heat oil in frying pan over med-high heat.

2. Add legumes and cook for 1–2 mins.

3. Transfer legumes, liquid and lemon juice to blender/food processor and blend to a smooth, thin puree consistency, adding extra liquid as required.

> ♀ Tip
>
> To make thicker purees use less liquid.

It is encouraged to offer non sweet vegetable purees in the first 1–2 weeks, before introducing sweet vegetable purees.

Non sweet vegetable options

Ingredients

zucchini, peeled and diced

broccoli, cut into small pieces

spinach leaves

eggplant, peeled and diced

beetroot, peeled and diced

asparagus, woody ends removed and cut into 1–2 cm lengths

mushrooms, sliced

green beans, ends removed and cut into 1–2 cm lengths

cauliflower, cut into small pieces

Sweet vegetable options

Ingredients

carrots, peeled and diced

sweet potato, peeled and diced

pumpkin, seeds removed, peeled and diced

potatoes, peeled and diced

frozen peas

🖉 Note

Although breastmilk and formula will add more nutrients to the puree, it will also make the vegetables taste sweeter. If you prefer to keep the vegetable puree savoury, try adding oil such as extra virgin olive oil or avocado oil. Healthy oils will provide good fats and nutrients.

Fresh vegetables

Method

1. Add vegetable to steamer and steam until tender:

- Around 5–10 mins for smaller vegetables e.g. peas or spinach

- 15–20 mins for larger diced vegetables e.g. potato or zucchini

- The vegetable is tender if a knife can slice through with ease

2. Blend vegetables in a food processor/blender to a thin puree consistency. Add oil/breastmilk/ formula or cooking liquid as needed to obtain the desired consistency.

Frozen vegetables

Method

1. Heat 1–2 tsp oil in frying pan over med-high heat

2. Add frozen vegetables and cook until warmed through, according to packet instructions

3. Blend vegetables in a food processor/blender to a smooth, thin puree consistency adding oil/ breastmilk/ formula or cooking liquid as needed to obtain the desired consistency.

To begin with you might like to remove the skin for a smoother puree. As your child develops their eating skills you may leave the skin on, as an abundance of fibre and nutrients are contained in the skin and directly under the skin.

Soft fruit options

banana

stone fruits e.g. peaches, plums, apricots and cherries

berries e.g. blueberries, strawberries, blackberries, raspberries

melons e.g.watermelon, rockmelon and honeydew

mango

figs

ripe pears

kiwi fruit

Method

1. Remove skin (if required) and any seed/s

2. Use food processor/blender to puree to thin consistency

Hard fruit options

firm pears

apples

Method

1. Peel and core fruit

2. Roughly dice

3. Add to steamer and steam until soft (around 5–10 mins)

4. Puree in a blender/food processor -if required, add liquid from steamer to obtain the desired consistency.

ALLERGEN RECIPES

Everything nut spread

Once you have introduced peanuts, tree nuts and sesame individually with no reaction, you may like to make a nut spread that includes all 3 allergens.

Ingredients

½ **cup** smooth, natural peanut butter (no added salt or sugar)*

2 tsp hulled tahini

½ **cup** ABC spread (combination of almond, brazil & cashew)

½ **cup** macadamia spread

Method

1. Place all ingredients in a large bowl and mix well to combine.

2. Store in a clean jar in the fridge

✎ Note

*Do not use peanut butters that state they are roasted as roasted peanuts are more likely to trigger an allergic reaction.[50]

To clean the jar, wash with dish liquid and fill with boiling water, allow it to sit until cooled, pour out water and let dry.

Soy and Sesame Hommus

Once you have introduced soy and sesame individually with no reaction, you may like to make a hommus that includes 2 allergens.

Ingredients

125g tin edamame beans, drained and rinsed

2 × 420g tins no added salt chickpeas OR cannellini beans, drained and rinsed

1 ½ large lemons, juiced

2 cloves garlic, crushed

1 tbsp hulled tahini

½ cup extra virgin olive oil

Method

1. Place all ingredients in a food processor and puree to a smooth consistency, adding extra oil or sterilized water if needed.

RECIPES FOR
ALL THE FAMILY

(including infants at every texture stage)

To make life easier, the recipes in this book have been devised so that everyone in the family can enjoy them, without the need to cook separate meals for infants. Each recipe includes guidelines for each texture stage, as well as optional additions for parents.

STOCK &
SPICE MIXES

Infants have immature kidneys, which means it is difficult for them to excrete excess salt from the body. This may cause high blood pressure, both in the short and long term. The use of salt is therefore not recommended. Many recipes, however, call for stock powder or spice mixes to provide flavour. Unfortunately, store bought varieties of all stock powders and many spice mixes (e.g. curry powder) contain high levels of sodium/salt and other unwanted ingredients such as 'flavour enhancers' and preservatives. For this reason, some simple recipes for healthy, salt free stocks and spice mixes are provided below. Not only will these help you create one pot wonders but they will also save time as they are prepared in bulk for later use. If you do, however, prefer to buy ready made stock or spice mixes, always look for the 'no added' or 'reduced' salt varieties.

NO SALT STOCK POWDER

Ingredients

- **40g** jar onion powder
- **3½ tbsp** garlic powder
- **3½ tbsp** paprika
- **3½ tbsp** mustard powder*
- **1½ tbsp** thyme leaves
- **2 tsp** white pepper

*Mustard powder can be found in supermarkets with curry powders or bags of spices.

To make stock powder

- Mix spices together and store in an airtight container.

To make stock:

- Add 2 tsp powder to 1 cup water.

 Note

Before adding powder to water, give the container a quick shake as heavier spices will naturally sink to the bottom of the container.

MEXICAN SPICE MIX

Ingredients

30g jar ground cumin

20g jar ground coriander

35g jar mild paprika

1½ tbsp ground oregano

1½ tbsp garlic powder

Method

- Mix spices together and store in an airtight container.

INDIAN SPICE MIX

Ingredients

2 × 20g jar ground coriander

2 × 30g jar ground cumin

2 × 30g jar ground turmeric

25g jar ground ginger

1½ tbsp mustard powder*

1 tbsp white pepper

1½ tbsp ground cinnamon

1 tbsp ground cardamom

1 tsp cayenne pepper

*Mustard powder can be found in supermarkets with curry powders or bags of spices.

Method

• Mix spices together and store in an airtight container.

MOROCCAN SPICE MIX

Ingredients

2 × 30g jar ground cumin

20g jar ground coriander

30g jar turmeric

2 tbsp garlic powder

Method

• Mix spices together and store in an airtight container.

BREAKFAST RECIPES

OVERNIGHT PORRIDGE

Ingredients

1 ½ cup rolled oats

2 cups full fat cow's milk

1 cup coconut water OR sterilised water

½ cup wheat infant cereal (e.g. *Nestle Cerelac Oats & Wheat With Prune Infant Cereal*)

5 to 6 medjool dates, pitted and finely chopped

Optional:

spices: cinnamon, nutmeg or allspice

soft fruit, e.g. banana, berries or ripe pear, figs (<0.5 cm in size)

'Everything nut spread'* OR tree nut spread* OR almond meal* OR LSA*

Parents: nuts and/or seeds

Allergens: cow's milk, wheat, sesame*, peanuts*, tree nuts*

Method

1. Place all ingredients (including any spice) into a microwave safe bowl or a saucepan and let sit in the fridge overnight.

2. In the morning heat up porridge:

   - Place microwave safe bowl in the microwave and cook on high for 3–5 mins or until warmed through OR

   - Place saucepan on the stove on medium-high heat and cook for 5 mins, or until warmed through.

Texture stage				
Puree	Mashed	Minced/finely chopped	Soft finger food	Parents
Blend in blender/ food processor until smooth puree consistency.	Pulse in a blender/ food processor until slightly pureed with small lumps. Optional: add mashed fruit and/or nut spread.	Serve as is. Optional: add mashed or finely chopped fruit (<0.5 cm in size) and/or nut spread.	Serve as is. Optional: add chopped fruit (4 cm × <1 cm) and/or nut spread.	Optional: add nuts and/or seeds

OVERNIGHT OATS

Ingredients

½ **cup** wheat infant cereal (e.g. *Nestle Cerelac Oats & Wheat With Prune Infant Cereal*)

¼ **cup** rolled oats

1 **cup** coconut water

½ **cup** full fat yoghurt (plain or fruit flavoured)

Optional:

fruit e.g. mashed mango, finely diced berries (<0.5 cm in size), finely grated apple or pear

2 tsp 'Everything nut spread'* OR tree nut spread* OR almond meal* OR LSA*

Parents: nuts, seeds and/or flaked coconut for serving

Allergens: wheat, cow's milk, sesame*, peanuts*, tree nuts*

Method

1. Combine all ingredients (including any fruit or nut spread or meals) in a bowl and store in the fridge overnight.

Texture stage				
Puree	Mashed	Minced/finely chopped	Soft finger food	Parents
Blend in a blender/food processor until smooth puree consistency.	Pulse in a blender/food processor until slightly pureed with small lumps.	Serve as is.		Optional: add nuts, seeds and/or flaked coconut.

SMOOTHIE BOWL

Ingredients

½ **cup** wheat infant cereal (e.g. *Nestle Cerelac Oats & Wheat With Prune Infant Cereal*)

1 cup fruit and/or vegetable e.g.

½ **cup** blueberries + **1** small banana ('kid' sized)

1 mango + **4** strawberries or mixed berries

Small handful baby spinach leaves, ¼ avocado and ½ small banana

1 cup liquid such as: full fat cow's* OR soy milk* OR coconut water

Optional:

extra fruit for serving

2 tsp 'Everything nut spread'* OR tree nut spread* OR almond meal* OR LSA*

Parents: nuts, seeds, granola, cereal, muesli or fruit for serving

> ♡ **Tip**
>
> Frozen fruit works just as well.

Allergens: wheat, cow's milk*, soy* sesame*, peanuts*, tree nuts*

Method

1. Blend all ingredients (including nut spread or meals) in a blender/food processor until smooth puree consistency.

Texture stage				
Puree	Mashed	Minced/finely chopped	Soft finger food	Parents
Serve as is.	Serve as is. Optional: top with mashed soft fruit.	Serve as is. Optional: top with finely chopped soft fruit (<0.5 cm in size).	Serve as is. Optional: top with chopped soft fruit (4 cm × <1 cm).	Optional: nuts, seeds, granola, cereal, muesli or fruit.

BANANA BREAD SLICE

Ingredients

4 large, ripe bananas (450 g), cut into chunks + extra mashed ripe banana to serve

3 medjool dates, pitted and roughly chopped

½ cup macadamia OR walnut oil

1 tsp cinnamon

2 tsp baking powder

1¾ cup desiccated coconut

1 cup almond meal OR LSA (ground linseed, sunflower seed & almonds)

¾ cup wheat infant cereal (e.g. *Nestle Cerelac Oats & Wheat With Prune Infant Cereal*)

2 eggs

Optional for serving:

- Parents: nut spread

Allergens: tree nut, wheat, egg

Method

1. Preheat oven to 160°C fan forced.

2. Line the base and sides of a 30 x 22 cm slice pan with baking paper.

3. Place all ingredients into a food processor and blend to a smooth consistency. (If you don't have a large enough food processor, just blend banana and medjool dates in the processor to a smooth consistency. Transfer banana and date mixture to a large bowl and combine with other ingredients, mixing well.)

4. Spoon batter into pan and smooth the surface. Cook in the oven for 50–60 mins, or until a skewer inserted in the centre comes out clean.

5. Leave in the pan for 30 mins, then turn onto a wire rack to cool completely.

6. Divide slice into 8 portions. Store in fridge and consume within 2 days. Freeze whatever is not immediately required for later use. Store in an airtight container in the freezer with baking paper between layers to prevent sticking.

Texture stage				
Puree	Mashed	Minced/finely chopped	Soft finger food	Parents
Blend slice portion and liquid (sterilized water, breastmilk or formula) in blender/food processor until smooth puree consistency.	Mash slice portion with the back of a fork. Add extra mashed, ripe banana and mix through.	Finely chop to <0.5 cm size or mash. Add extra mashed, ripe banana and mix through.	Cut into pinky finger sized strips (4 cm x <1 cm).	Optional: top with nut spread.

LUNCH AND DINNER RECIPES

EASY PEASY SCRAMBLE

Ingredients

4 eggs

1 tbsp extra virgin olive oil

½ **cup** frozen Veggie Rice (e.g. *Birds Eye Veggie Rice: carrot, cauliflower, broccoli*)

½ **cup** frozen peas

To serve: soy and sesame hommus* OR store bought hommus (e.g. *Obela Hommus Smooth Classic*)

Allergens: egg, sesame, soy*

Method

1. Lightly whisk eggs in a bowl.

2. Add oil to frying pan and heat over med-high heat.

3. Add frozen vegetables and cook for 3 mins.

4. Add eggs to vegetables and stir regularly until cooked through (1–2 mins).

5. Combine scrambled egg and hommus.

Texture stage				
Puree	Mashed	Minced/finely chopped	Soft finger food	Parents
Blend scrambled egg & hommus in a blender/food processor until smooth puree consistency.	Mash scrambled egg and hommus.		Serve as is.	Add seasoning such as salt, pepper and chilli to taste.

BUTTER CHICKEN

Ingredients

½ **cup** (80g) unsalted, raw cashews

1 red onion, roughly chopped

5 cloves garlic

40g fresh ginger (approx 7 cm length), sliced

2 tbsp butter (or extra virgin olive oil)

2 tbsp Indian Spice Mix

2 pinches (⅛ tsp) ground cardamom

1 pinch ground cloves

1 BBQ chicken, skin removed, meat pulled off, finely shredded and chopped to <0.5x1 cm pieces (be careful to remove all bones)

⅓ **cup** (100g) tomato paste

250g frozen *Veggie Rice* (e.g. *Birds Eye Veggie Rice: carrot, cauliflower, broccoli*) OR **2x** grated carrots + **1x** grated zucchini

300ml full fat cream

grains such as quinoa OR rice e.g. long grain brown

Optional

• Parents: naan bread

Allergens: tree nuts, cow's milk

Method

1. Cook grain according to packet instructions.

2. Blend cashews in a food processor to a fine consistency. Remove and set aside in a bowl.

3. Place onion, garlic and ginger in the food processor and blend until finely diced.

4. Heat butter in a large saucepan over med-high heat. Add onion mixture, Indian spice mix, cardamom and cloves and cook for 5 mins.

5. Add chicken, tomato paste, *Veggie Rice*/vegetables and ground cashews and cook for 2–3 mins, or until vegetables are warmed through and tender.

6. Add cream and cook for 3 mins.

Texture stage				
Puree	Mashed	Minced/finely chopped	Soft finger food	Parents
Blend butter chicken and grain in a blender/food processor until smooth puree consistency.	Pulse grain and butter chicken in a blender/food processor until slightly pureed with small lumps.	Combine butter chicken with grain, mixing well. Finely chop to <0.5 cm size.	Combine butter chicken with grain, mixing well.	Add seasoning such as salt, pepper and chilli to taste. Serve with grain or naan bread.

SATAY

Ingredients

3 large carrots, roughly chopped

1 large red onion, roughly chopped

3 stalks celery, roughly chopped

1 tbsp oil (e.g. extra virgin olive oil)

¾ cup smooth peanut butter

½ tbsp tamarind puree

80g lemongrass paste

1 cup water

1 BBQ chicken, skin removed, meat pulled off, finely shredded and chopped to <0.5x1 cm pieces (be careful to remove all bones)

grains such as quinoa OR rice e.g. long grain brown

Allergens: peanuts

Method

1. Cook grain according to packet instructions.

2. Blend carrot, onion and celery in a food processor to almost a puree consistency.

3. Heat oil in a large pot or frying pan over med-high heat.

4. Add carrot mixture to pot and cook for 5 mins.

5. Add peanut butter, tamarind, lemongrass and water and cook for 4–5 mins, or until the sauce thickens.

6. Add chicken and warm through.

Texture stage				
Puree	Mashed	Minced/finely chopped	Soft finger food	Parents
Blend satay and grain in a blender/ food processor until smooth puree consistency.	Pulse grain and satay in blender/ food processor until slightly pureed with small lumps.	Combine satay with grain, mixing well. Finely chop to <0.5 cm size.	Combine satay with grain, mixing well.	Add seasoning such as salt, pepper and chilli to taste. Serve with chosen grain.

MOROCCAN SALMON WITH PEARL COUSCOUS SALAD

Ingredients

1–2 tbsp extra virgin olive oil

2 large zucchini, grated

1 large eggplant, grated

1 cup pearl couscous + **1¼ cup** sterilized water

1 tbsp Moroccan Spice Mix + **2 tsp** extra

4x 100–120g skinless salmon portions

1 large handful mint leaves, finely chopped

1 large handful coriander, finely chopped

4 spring onion, finely chopped

juice and zest of **1** lemon

hommus to serve (homemade or store bought e.g. *Obela Hommus Smooth Classic*)

Allergens: fish, sesame

Method

1. Preheat oven to 180°C fan forced.

2. Line an oven tray with baking paper.

3. Heat oil in a large saucepan over medium-high heat.

4. Add zucchini and eggplant and cook for 4–5 mins or until tender/soft.

5. Add pearl couscous, 1¼ cup water and moroccan spice mix and bring to a boil. Reduce heat and simmer, lid on for 10–15 mins, or until couscous is cooked.

6. Place salmon on oven tray and sprinkle with 2 tsp moroccan spice mix, coating evenly.

7. Cook salmon in oven for 9–15 mins, until cooked through.

8. In a large bowl, combine pearl couscous mixture, mint, coriander, spring onion, lemon juice and zest and mix well.

9. To serve, top couscous mixture with salmon and hommus.

Texture stage				
Puree	Mashed	Minced/finely chopped	Soft finger food	Parents
Blend couscous mixture, salmon and hommus in a blender/food processor until smooth puree consistency.	Pulse couscous mixture, salmon and hommus in a blender/food processor until slightly pureed with small lumps.	Combine salmon and couscous, mixing well. Finely chop to <0.5 cm size. Mix through hommus.	Flake salmon into small pieces (4 cm × <1 cm). Combine salmon and couscous. Mix through hommus.	Add seasoning such as salt, pepper and chilli to taste.

MEXICAN MINCE

Ingredients

½ **tbsp** extra virgin olive oil

1 onion, finely diced

500g mince (beef, pork OR chicken)

400g can no added salt diced tomatoes

1 tbsp tomato paste

2 tbsp Mexican Spice Mix

2 cups frozen peas, carrot and corn mix

½ **cup** full fat shredded tasty cheese

Optional toppings: full fat sour cream, mashed avocado

Parent serving options: chopped coriander, lime juice, tortillas, tacos, tortilla strips.

Method

1. Heat oil in large frying pan or saucepan over med-high heat.

2. Add onion and cook until softened, 5 mins.

3. Add mince and cook for 5 mins or until browned and cooked.

4. Add tinned tomatoes, tomato paste, mexican spice mix, peas, carrot & corn mix, reduce heat and simmer for 5–10 mins.

5. Turn off heat, add cheese and mix through.

Allergens: cow's milk

Texture stage				
Puree	Mashed	Minced/finely chopped	Soft finger food	Parents
Blend in blender/ food processor until smooth puree consistency.	Pulse in blender/ food processor until slightly pureed with small lumps Optional: top with sour cream and/or mashed avocado.	Pulse in a blender/ food processor until slightly mashed. Optional: top with sour cream and/or mashed avocado. Note: corn has a hard skin and therefore may pose a choking risk, therefore, by slightly pulsing food it will break the corn into more manageable pieces to reduce choking risk.	Pulse in a blender/ food processor until slightly mashed. Optional: top with sour cream and/or mashed avocado. Add strips of soft tacos cut into pinky finger sized strips (4 cm × <1 cm).	Add seasoning such as salt, pepper and chilli to taste. Serve with desired side such as tortillas, tacos or tortilla strips. Top with avocado, coriander, lime juice and sour cream.

SPEEDY MEXI-BEANS

This recipe is great on its own or with soft tacos (or tortilla strips for parents).

Ingredients

Bean mixture

2 × 400g cans no added salt black beans, rinsed and drained

4 spring onions, green part only, thinly sliced

2 tsp Mexican Spice Mix

400g can no added salt diced tomatoes

Guacamole

1 ripe avocado, deseeded, mashed

1 tomato, finely diced

juice of **½–1** lime

Optional toppings: full fat sour cream, shredded full fat tasty cheese

Optional
- Parents: corn chips, tortilla strip, wrap, tacos OR rice

Method

1. Add black beans to a microwave safe bowl, mash beans with the back of a fork, until roughly mashed.

2. Add spring onion, spice mix and tinned tomatoes to bowl, and combine.

3. Cook bean mixture in microwave for 5 mins on high heat.

4. Whilst beans are cooking combine all guacamole ingredients in a bowl.

Allergens: cow's milk

Texture stage				
Puree	Mashed	Minced/finely chopped	Soft finger food	Parents
Combine bean mixture with guacamole and blend in blender/ food processor until smooth puree consistency.	Combine bean mixture with guacamole and pulse in a blender/ food processor until slightly pureed with small lumps. Optional topping: full fat sour cream.	Combine bean mixture with guacamole and pulse in a blender/ food processor until slightly mashed. Optional topping: full fat sour cream.	Combine bean mixture with guacamole, mashing any large pieces of tomato. Optional: • full fat sour cream • full fat shredded cheese • soft tacos cut into pinky finger sized strips (4 cm × <1 cm).	Add seasoning such as salt, pepper and chilli to taste. Add guacamole Serve with: • tortilla strips/ corn chips • wraps • soft or hard tacos • rice

SHEPHERD'S PIE

Ingredients

Beef mixture

1 large onion, roughly chopped

3 large carrots, roughly chopped

3 sticks celery, roughly chopped

1 tbsp extra virgin olive oil

500g beef mince

4 cloves garlic, crushed

4 tbsp tomato paste

⅓ **cup** water

1 tbsp No Salt Stock Powder OR **2** salt-reduced beef stock cubes

Topping

2 × 400g cans no added salt cannellini beans

⅓ **cup** grated parmesan

⅓ **cup** full fat milk

2 tbsp extra virgin olive oil

Allergens: cow's milk

Method

1. Place onion, carrot, celery into a food processor and pulse to a finely chopped consistency.

2. Heat oil in a large oven proof pot* over med-high heat.

3. Add onion mixture and cook for 5 mins.

4. Add beef mince & garlic and cook for 5 mins or until browned and cooked through.

5. Add tomato paste, water, stock powder and cook for 1–2 mins, turn off heat.

6. Turn oven on to grill.

7. Place all topping ingredients into a food processor and blend to a smooth consistency.

8. Top beef mixture with mash and place in oven to grill for 5–10 mins or until golden .

 Tip

*If you don't have an ovenproof pot, transfer cooked beef mixture into an oven dish and top with topping before grilling.

Texture stage				
Puree	Mashed	Minced/finely chopped	Soft finger food	Parents
Blend in a blender/food processor until smooth puree consistency.	Mash meal with back of fork.	Serve as is.	Serve as is.	Add seasoning such as salt, pepper and chilli to taste.

PESTO PASTA

Ingredients

3 cups of pasta e.g. risoni, spiral pasta, penne OR rigatoni. **Refer to the table below for the appropriate pasta to use at each texture stage.**

70g grated parmesan

¼ cup shelled edamame beans (if frozen, thaw)

50g spinach (fresh OR frozen, thawed)

½ head (170g) broccoli, roughly chopped

1 cup soft nuts e.g. pine nuts, cashews, macadamias, almond meal, LSA OR a blend of any of these

1 large bunch (40g) basil leaves, stems removed

½ cup extra virgin olive oil + **1 tbsp** extra for cooking

2 garlic cloves

1 leek, white part only, roughly chopped

juice (**¼ cup**) and zest of **1** lemon

Optional parent additions: grilled chicken, tinned

tuna, cooked prawns

Method

1. Cook pasta according to packet instructions.

2. Blend pesto ingredients in a food processor or blender to a smooth consistency.

3. Heat 1 tbsp of extra virgin olive oil in a large pot over med-high heat.

4. Add pesto mixture and cook for 5 mins (or until garlic and leek are cooked through).

Allergens: cow's milk, soy, tree nut, wheat

 Note

This recipe makes a large quantity of pesto, so you might like to freeze some, or use it as a bread or pizza topping etc.

Texture stage				
Puree	Mashed	Minced/finely chopped	Soft finger food	Parents
Blend pesto and any pasta in a blender/food processor until smooth puree consistency.	Pulse any pasta and pesto in a blender/ food processor until slightly pureed with small lumps.	Combine pesto with risoni, mixing well.	Combine pesto with spiral pasta, penne or rigatoni, mixing well.	Add seasoning such as salt, pepper and chilli to taste.

VEGGIE PACKED MAC AND CHEESE

Ingredients

Pasta mixture

2 cups macaroni, penne OR rigatoni

500g frozen *Veggies Rice* (e.g. *Birds Eye Veggie Rice: cauliflower, carrot, broccoli*), cooked according to packet instructions **OR 500g** cooked cauliflower, carrot and broccoli, finely chopped

150g 3 or 4 cheese blend shredded cheese

150g full fat ricotta

50g grated parmesan

300ml full fat cream

1 tsp thyme

Topping

⅓ cup extra virgin olive oil

1 cup bread crumbs (wholemeal if available)

2 cloves garlic, crushed

1 tsp smoked paprika

zest of **2** lemons

1 tsp thyme

Optional: pinch of cayenne

Method

1. Preheat oven to 180°C fan forced.

2. Cook pasta according to packet instruction.

3. Place cooked pasta, veggies, shredded cheese, ricotta, parmesan, cream, and thyme in a 30 cm × 22 cm oven dish, mixing well to combine. Once combined, smooth surface.

4. Combine all topping ingredients in a bowl, mixing well.

5. Spoon topping ingredients over pasta mixture, spreading evenly.

6. Place in oven and cook for 10 mins.

7. Turn oven on to grill and cook for another 5 mins under grill.

Allergens: wheat, cow's milk

Texture stage				
Puree	Mashed	Minced/finely chopped	Soft finger food	Parents
Blend in a blender/food processor until smooth puree consistency.	Pulse in a blender/food processor until slightly pureed with small lumps.	Finely chop to <0.5 cm size.	Serve as is.	Add seasoning such as salt, pepper and chilli to taste.

SEAFOOD PIE

Ingredients

2 large sweet potatoes

1 large carrot, roughly chopped

2 sticks celery, roughly chopped

260g raw prawns, peeled, deveined

180g 3 or 4 cheese blend shredded cheese

460g skinless salmon portions, cut into 2 cm × 2 cm pieces

juice and zest of **2** lemons

2 ripe tomatoes, finely diced

1 large bunch parsley, finely chopped.

1 tbsp No Salt Stock Powder

1 tsp smoked paprika

Allergens: shellfish, fish, cow's milk

Method

1. Preheat oven to 200°C fan forced.

2. Pierce sweet potatoes with a fork on all sides. Microwave on high for 4 mins. Turn sweet potatoes over and cook for a further 4 mins. Continue turning and cooking sweet potatoes in the microwave until very tender (easily pierced with a fork). Allow to cool.

3. Place carrot, celery and prawns into a food processor and blend until finely chopped/grated. Remove and place in a large, deep pie dish or 30 cm × 22 cm oven dish.

4. Add cheese, salmon, lemon juice and zest, tomatoes, parsley, stock powder and smoked paprika. Mix through to combine.

5. Remove flesh from sweet potato and place in bowl. Discard skin.

6. Mash sweet potato and top fish pie.

7. Place in oven and cook for 40 mins (or until salmon/prawns cooked through).

Texture stage				
Puree	Mashed	Minced/finely chopped	Soft finger food	Parents
Blend in a blender/food processor until smooth puree consistency.	Mash with back of fork or pulse in a blender/food processor until slightly pureed with small lumps.	Mash with back of fork or finely chop to <0.5 cm size.	Serve as is.	Add seasoning such as salt, pepper and chilli to taste.

ONE PAN
WONDERS

CREAMY LEMON SALMON RISONI

Ingredients

1½ cups (305g) risoni

zest of **2** lemons, juice of **1** lemon

4 tsp No Salt Stock Powder + **2 cups** boiling hot water **OR 2 cups** (500ml) reduced-salt vegetable stock

⅔ cup (160ml) full fat cream

2 cup frozen mixed *Veggie Rice* (e.g. *Birds Eye Veggie Rice: carrot, cauliflower, broccoli*) **OR 1** large grated carrot and 2 large grated zucchinis

½ cup frozen peas

2 green shallots, thinly sliced

4 × 100g skinless salmon portions

large handful of mint, stems removed, finely chopped

Allergens: wheat, cow's milk, fish

Method

1. Preheat oven to 170°C fan forced.

2. Place risoni, lemon zest, stock powder, boiling water and cream in a 30 cm × 22 cm oven dish and mix well to combine.

3. Cover with foil and cook in oven for 20 mins.

4. Remove from oven and carefully remove foil, add veggie rice, peas, shallots and mix well to combine.

5. Top risoni mixture with salmon and place back in the oven to cook for 15–20 mins (or until salmon is cooked through).

6. Add lemon juice and mint and mix well.

Texture stage				
Puree	Mashed	Minced/finely chopped	Soft finger food	Parents
Blend in blender/food processor until smooth puree consistency.	Pulse in a blender/food processor until slightly pureed with small lumps.	Mash with back of fork or finely chop to <0.5 cm size.	Flake salmon into small pieces (4 cm × <1 cm).	Add seasoning such as salt, pepper and chilli to taste.

MUSHROOM CHICKEN RISOTTO

Ingredients

1–2 tbsp extra virgin olive oil

1 large onion, finely chopped

370g button mushrooms, thinly sliced

2 cloves garlic, crushed/minced

250g arborio rice

100g white quinoa

1 BBQ chicken, skin removed, meat pulled off, finely shredded and chopped to <0.5x2 cm pieces (be careful to remove all bones)

250g 3 or 4 cheese blend shredded cheese

8 tsp No Salt Stock Powder + **1L** water **OR 1L** salt-reduced chicken stock

1 large bunch parsley, finely chopped

Allergens: cow's milk

Method

1. Preheat oven to 180°C fan forced.

2. Heat oil in an oven safe pot* over med-high heat on stove top.

3. Add onion and cook for 3–5 mins or until onion has softened.

4. Add mushrooms and garlic and cook for 2–3 mins or until mushrooms have softened.

5. Add rice, quinoa, chicken, cheese, stock powder and water and bring to boil.

6. Turn off heat, place lid on pot and put in the oven for 30 mins, or until rice/quinoa has absorbed all the liquid.*

7. Top with parsley.

> ### ♀ Tip
>
> *If you do not have an oven proof pot, transfer the final mixture into an oven dish and cover with foil before cooking in the oven for 30 mins.

Texture stage				
Puree	Mashed	Minced/finely chopped	Soft finger food	Parents
Blend in blender/ food processor until smooth puree consistency.	Pulse in a blender/ food processor until slightly pureed with small lumps.	Finely chop to <0.5 cm size.	Serve as is.	Add seasoning such as salt, pepper and chilli to taste.

CORN FRITTERS

Ingredients

Fritter ingredients

1 × 420g can creamed corn

1 cup self raising wholemeal flour

4 eggs

1 tbsp Mexican Spice Mix

1 × 420g can no added salt black beans, drained, rinsed & slightly mashed

¼ cup shredded full fat tasty cheese

2 tbsp full fat milk

Topping ingredients

avocado

cherry tomatoes, cut into ⅛ OR ¼ depending on size

fresh lime juice

optional: fresh coriander leaves, finely chopped

Optional:

Parents: tabasco sauce

Method

1. Preheat oven to 180°C fan forced.

2. Line 2–3 oven trays with baking paper.

3. Combine fritter ingredients in a large bowl.

4. Place ¼ cup portions of batter onto lined tray, using the bottom of the measuring cup to flatten slightly (around <1 cm high).

5. Cook in oven for 10–12 mins, or until firm to touch.

Allergens: wheat, eggs, cow's milk

Texture stage				
Puree	Mashed	Minced/finely chopped	Soft finger food	Parents
Blend fritter(s) and desired amount of toppings in a blender/food processor until smooth puree consistency, adding extra lime juice as required.	Pulse fritter(s) and desired amount of toppings in a blender/food processor and pulse until slightly pureed with small lumps, adding extra lime juice as required.	Combine fritter(s) and desired amount of toppings and finely chop to <0.5 cm or slightly pulse in blender/food processor.	Cut fritter(s) into pinky finger sized strips (4 cm × <1 cm) and top with desired amount of toppings.	Add seasoning such as salt, pepper and chilli to taste. Optional: tabasco sauce.

BEETROOT PATTIES

Ingredients

500g fresh beetroot (around 2–3), peeled and roughly chopped

1 bunch mint, stems removed

1 bunch parsley

1 bunch dill (30g)

4 spring onion, green part only

zest of **2** lemons (+ juice for pureeing/mashing)

2 tbsp tahini

2 eggs

1 tbsp Moroccan Spice Mix

1 ¼ cup almond meal

1 × 400g can no added salt lentils, rinsed and drained

¾ cup iron fortified wheat infant cereal (e.g. *Nestle Cerelac Oats & Wheat With Prune Infant Cereal*)

Optional:

- Tzatziki to serve with soft finger food

- Parents: baby spinach, rocket leaves, halloumi, tzatziki

Method

1. Preheat oven to 180°C fan forced.

2. Line 2–3 oven trays with baking paper.

3. Blend beetroot, mint, parsley, dill, spring onion, lemon zest, tahini, eggs and spice mix in a food processor to a smooth consistency (blend in batches if you have a smaller food processor).

4. Transfer beetroot batter to a large bowl and add almond meal, lentils & infant cereal. Mix well to combine.

5. Place ⅓ cup portions of batter onto lined tray, using the bottom of the measuring cup to flatten slightly (around 1 cm high).

6. Cook in oven for 20–25 mins, or until slightly firm to touch.

Allergens: sesame, eggs, tree nut, wheat

Texture stage				
Puree	Mashed	Minced/finely chopped	Soft finger food	Parents
Blend patty(ies) and lemon juice (enough to moisten patty) in a blender/food processor until smooth puree consistency.	Pulse patty(ies) and lemon juice (enough to moisten patty) in a blender/food processor until slightly pureed OR mash patty(ies) using enough lemon juice to moisten.	Finely chop patty(ies) to <0.5 cm in size or slightly pulse in a blender/food processor.	Cut patty(ies) into pinky finger sized strips (4 cm × <1 cm). Optional: top with tzatziki.	Add seasoning such as salt, pepper and chilli to taste. Serve with baby spinach, rocket leaves, pan fried halloumi and tzatziki.

SNACKS
(10 MONTHS+)

BUBU BERRY MUFFINS

Ingredients

2 cups almond meal OR LSA

½ tsp baking soda

1 cup wheat infant cereal (e.g. *Nestle Cerelac Oats & Wheat With Prune Infant cereal*)

zest of **3** lemons

2 eggs

¼ cup blueberries (fresh OR frozen) + ¾ cup extra

2 tsp vanilla bean paste

½ cup coconut flavoured yoghurt

½ cup oil (macadamia, walnut OR coconut oil)

5 medjool dates, pitted

Allergens: tree nut, wheat, egg, cow's milk

Method

1. Preheat the oven to 160°C fan forced.

2. Line a 12 capacity muffin tray with muffin cases.

3. Blend all ingredients in a food processor until smooth. (If you don't have a large enough food processor, blend blueberries, yoghurt and medjool dates, remove and combine well with other ingredients in a large bowl). Note, mixture will appear dry at this stage.

4. Transfer mixture into a large bowl and mix through extra blueberries.

5. Spoon mixture into prepared muffin tray. Bake for 35–40 mins, or until a skewer inserted in the centre comes out clean.

6. Leave in the muffin tray until cooled completely.

7. Store in fridge for up to 2 days. Freeze whatever is not immediately required for later use.

8. When serving, cut into approximately 4 cm × <1 cm strips.

PEAR, RASPBERRY & COCONUT SLICE

Ingredients

2 cups almond meal OR LSA

1 cup desiccated coconut

½ **tsp** baking soda

2 eggs

1 cup (125g) raspberries (fresh OR frozen)

½ **cup** full fat strawberry flavoured yoghurt

½ **cup** oil (macadamia OR walnut)

1 ripe pear, cored and grated

Allergens: tree nut, egg, cow's milk

Method

1. Preheat the oven to 160°C fan forced.

2. Line a 30 cm × 22 cm baking pan with baking paper.

3. Combine all ingredients in a large bowl, mixing well.

4. Spoon into the prepared pan and smooth the surface. Bake for 40–50 mins, or until a skewer inserted in the centre comes out clean.

5. Leave in the pan until cooled completely.

6. Divide slice into 8 portions. Store in fridge and consume within 2 days. Freeze whatever is not immediately required for later use. Store in an airtight container in the freezer with baking paper between layers to prevent sticking.

7. When serving, cut into approximately 4 cm × <1 cm strips.

CORN BREAD SLICE

Ingredients

1 × 420g can creamed corn

4 spring onions, green part only, thinly sliced

½ cup extra virgin olive oil

1 tsp baking powder

2 cups almond meal

1 cup wheat infant cereal (e.g. *Nestle Cerelac Oats & Wheat With Prune Infant Cereal*)

2 eggs

Allergens: tree nut, wheat, egg

Method

1. Preheat the oven to 160°C fan forced.

2. Line the base and sides of a 30 cm × 22 cm baking pan with baking paper.

3. Combine all ingredients in a large bowl, mixing well.

4. Spoon into the prepared pan and smooth the surface. Bake for 40–45 mins, or until a skewer inserted in the centre comes out clean.

5. Leave in the pan until cooled completely.

6. Divide slice into 8 portions. Store in fridge and consume within 2 days. Freeze whatever is not immediately required for later use. Store in an airtight container in the freezer with baking paper between layers to prevent sticking.

7. When serving, cut into approximately 4 cm × <1 cm strips.

IRRESISTIBLE NUTTER BUTTER SLICE

Note this slice has a firmer consistency. Therefore, use your judgement as to whether your 10 month old is developmentally ready to consume this texture. Beware, this slice truly is irresistible to infants and parents alike. One piece is never enough.

Ingredients

12 medjool dates, pitted

½ **cup** smooth peanut butter (or other nut spreads e.g. macadamia spread, everything nut spread)

1 cup desiccated coconut

Optional: try adding 1 tbsp cocoa OR cacao for a choc peanut butter flavour

Allergens: peanuts and/or tree nut

Method

1. Line a slice pan (28 cm × 19 cm) with baking paper, overhanging the sides.

2. Blend all ingredients in a food processor until well combined and mixture resembles coarse breadcrumb-like consistency.

3. Press the mixture firmly into the base of a baking pan using the excess baking paper to push the ingredients down. Flatten surface.

4. Place in the fridge for 30 mins.

5. Divide slice into 6 portions. Store in fridge and consume within 2 days. Freeze whatever is not immediately required for later use. Store in an airtight container in the freezer with baking paper between layers to prevent sticking.

6. When serving: cut into 0.5 cm × 4 cm strips.

 Tip

Slice may be very firm when first taken out of the fridge. Allow to sit for 3–5 mins at room temp to help soften for cutting.

ABOUT THE AUTHOR

Lindsey Jude is a senior Dietitian who graduated from the University of Sydney with a Bachelor of Science (Nutrition) Honours Class I. She became a dietitian as she is passionate about helping people improve their quality of life. Lindsey has worked across multiple settings in both private practice and the public health system. After the birth of her first child in 2020, Lindsey realised that there was a need for more information to be available to the general public about infant nutrition.

This book arose out of her desire to fill that need. Some of the information she discovered in her extensive research, including consultation with paediatric occupational and speech therapists, surprised and shocked even her. Her research was driven by personal need and allowed her to feel confident in the decisions she made regarding her own son's diet. She hopes that this book helps other parents negotiate the first year of their newborn's life more easily and confidently.

ACKNOWLEDGEMENTS

A huge thank you goes out to my family, for all their support and guidance. For my Mum who spent countless hours editing, to my husband who pushed me to write this book, and to my son, who inspired this book.

Thank you Jenny and Michelle for your expert advice on texture modifications and sensory preferences in infants. To Kia and Mila for being my guinea pigs and providing feedback. To my photographer, Helena, for helping my vision come to life, and providing recommendations and feedback on recipes. Lastly to Gideon for all the time, effort, amazing drawings & design! You exceeded my expectations and I could not be happier with the final result.

BIBLIOGRAPHY

1. Fewtrell, M., Bronsky, J., Campoy, C., Domellöf, M., Embleton, N., Fidler Mis, N., Hojsak, I., Hulst, J. M., Indrio, F., Lapillonne, A., & European Society for Paediatric Gastroenterology, Hepatology, and Nutrition (ESPGHAN). (2017, Jan). Complementary Feeding: A Position Paper by the European Society for Paediatric Gastroenterology, Hepatology, and Nutrition (ESPGHAN) Committee on Nutrition. *J Pediatr Gastroenterol Nutr, 64*(1), 119-132.

2. Wachs, T. D., Pollitt, E., Cueto, S., Jacoby, E., & Creed-Kanashiro, H. (2005, Mar). Relation of neonatal iron status to individual variability in neonatal temperament. *Dev Psychobiol, 46*(2), 141-53.

3. Beard, J. L. (2008, Dec). Why Iron Deficiency Is Important in Infant Development. *The Journal of Nutrition, 138*(12), 2534–2536.

4. National Health and Medical Research Council, Australian Government Department of Health and Ageing, New Zealand Ministry of Health. Nutrient Reference Values for Australia and New Zealand. Canberra: National Health and Medical Research Council; 2006.

5. Domellöf, M., Braegger, C., Campoy, C., Colomb, V., Decsi, T., Fewtrell, M., Hojsak, I., Mihatsch, W., Molgaard, C., Shamir, R., Turck, D., van Goudoever, J., & ESPGHAN Committee on Nutrition. (2014, Jan). Iron requirements of infants and toddlers. *J Pediatr Gastroenterol Nutr, 58*(1), 119-29.

6. Agostoni, C., Decsi, T., Fewtrell, M., Goulet, O., Kolacek, S., Koletzko, B., Fleischer Michaelsen, K., Moreno, L., Puntis, J., Rigo, J., Shamir, R., Szajewska, H., Turck, D., van Goudoever, J., & ESPGHAN Committee. (2008, Jan). Complementary feeding: a commentary by the ESPGHAN Committee on Nutrition. *J Pediatr Gastroenterol Nutr, 46*(1), 99-110.

7. National Health and Medical Research Council (2012) Infant Feeding Guidelines. Canberra: National Health and Medical Research Council.

8. National Health and Medical Research Council (2013) Australian Dietary Guidelines. Canberra: National Health and Medical Research Council.

9. Roduit, C., Frei, R., Depner, M., & Schuab, B. (2014, Apr). Increased food diversity in the first year of life is inversely associated with allergic diseases. *The Journal of allergy and clinical immunology, 133*(4), 1056-1064.

10. Wang, X., Ouyang, Y., Liu, J., Zhu, M., Zhao, G., Bao, W., & B Hu, F. (2014, Jul). Fruit and vegetable consumption and mortality from all causes, cardiovascular disease, and cancer: systematic review and dose-response meta-analysis of prospective cohort studies. *BMJ;349:g4490.*

11. Martínez-González, M. Á., Fuente-Arrillaga, C. d. l., López-Del-Burgo, C., Vázquez-Ruiz, Z., Benito, S., & Ruiz-Canela, M. (2011, Dec). Low consumption of fruit and vegetables and risk of chronic disease: a review of the epidemiological evidence and temporal trends among Spanish graduates. *Public Health Nutr, 14*(12A), 2309-2315.

12. Dauchet, L., Amouyel, P., Hercberg, S., & Dallongeville, J. (2006, Oct). Fruit and vegetable consumption and risk of coronary heart disease: a meta-analysis of cohort studies. *J Nutr, 136*(10), 2588-2593.

13. Whyte, A., Schafer, G., & Williams, C. (2016, Sep). Cognitive effects following acute wild blueberry supplementation in 7- to 10-year-old children. *Eur J Nutr, 55*(6), 2151-2162.

14. Khalid, S., Barfoot, K., May, G., Lamport, D., Reynolds, S., & Williams, C. (2017, Feb). Effects of Acute Blueberry Flavonoids on Mood in Children and Young Adults. *Nutrients, 9*(2), 158.

15. Public Health Scotland. (2020). Fun First Foods: An easy guide to introducing solids foods. Public Health Scotland.

16. Hathcock, J. N., Hattan, D. G., Jenkins, M. Y., McDonald, J. T., Sundaresan, P. R., & Wilkening, V. L. (1990, Aug). Evaluation of vitamin A toxicity. *Am J Clin Nutr, 52*(2), 183-202.

17. Tan, J., McKenzie, C., Vuillermin, P., Mebius, R., Macia, L., & Mackay, C. (2016, Jun). Dietary Fiber and Bacterial SCFA Enhance Oral Tolerance and Protect against Food Allergy through Diverse Cellular Pathways. *Cell Reports, 15*(12), 2809-2821.

18. Ferrante, G., Carta, M., Montante, C., Notarbartolo, V., Corsello, G., & Guiffre, M. (2020, Aug). Current Insights on Early Life Nutrition and Prevention of Allergy. *Frontiers in Pediatrics, 6*(8), 448.

19. Reynolds, E. H. (22, Jun). Folic acid, ageing, depression, and dementia. *BMJ, 324*(7352), 1512-1515.

20. Stevenson, L., Phillips, F., O'sullivan, K., & Walton, J. (2012, Dec). Wheat bran: its composition and benefits to health, a European perspective. *International Journal of Food Sciences and Nutrition, 63*(8), 1001-1013.

21. Fardet, A. (2010, Jun). New hypotheses for the health-protective mechanisms of whole-grain cereals: what is beyond fibre? *Nutr Res Rev, 23*(1), 65-134.

22. Smithers, L., Golley, R., Mittinty, M., Brazionis, L., Northstone, K., Emmett, P., & Lynch, J. (2012, Jul). Dietary patterns at 6, 15 and 24 months of age are associated with IQ at 8 years of age. *Eur J Epidemiol, 27*(7), 525-535.

23. Cancer Council. (n.d.). *Red meat, processed meat and cancer.* Cancer Council. Retrieved june 12, 2021, from https://www.cancercouncil.com.au/1in3cancers/lifestyle-choices-and-cancer/red-meat-processed-meat-and-cancer/.

24. Lifshitz, L., Ament, M., Kleinman, R., Klish, W., Lebenthal, E., Perman, J., & Udall Jr, J. (1992, May). Role of juice carbohydrate malabsorption in chronic nonspecific diarrhea in children. *J Pediatr, 120*(5), 825-829.

25. Rahman, M., Ng, J., & Naidu, R. (2009, April). Chronic exposure of arsenic via drinking water and its adverse health impacts on humans. *Environ Geochem Health, 31*(1), 189-200.

26. Hojsak, I., Braegger, C., Bronsky, J., Campoy, C., Colomb, V., Decsi, T., Domellof, M., Fewtrell, M., Fidler Mis, N., Mihatsch, W., Molgaard, C., Van Goudoever, J., & ESPGHAN Committee on Nutrition. (2015, Jan). Arsenic in rice: a cause for concern. *J Pediatr Gastroenterol Nutr, 60*(1), 142-145.

27. Wang, S., Wang, Z., Cheng, X., Li, J., Sang, Z., Zhang, X., Han, L., Qiao, X., Wu, Z., & Wang, Z. (2007, Apr). Arsenic and fluoride exposure in drinking water: children's IQ and growth in Shanyin county, Shanxi province, China. *Environ Health Perspect, 115*(4), 643-647.

28. Temme, E., & Van Hoydonck, P. (2002, May). Tea consumption and iron status. *Eur J Clin Nutr, 56*(5), 379-386.

29. National Allergy Strategy. (n.d.). *Why introduce food allergens before your baby is one?* NIP Allergies in the Bub. Retrieved Jun 12, 2021, from https://preventallergies.org.au/.

30. Fleischer, D. (2017, Mar). Life after LEAP: How to implement advice on introducing peanuts in early infancy. *J Pediatr Child Health, 53*(S1), 3-9.

31. Caffarelli, C., Mauro, D., Mastrorilli, C., Bottau, P., Cipriani, F., & Ricci, G. (2018, Nov). Solid Food Introduction and the Development of Food Allergies. *Nutrients, 10*(11), 1790.

32. Chan, E., Abrams, E., Hildebrand, K., & Watson, W. (2014, Apr). Early introduction of foods to prevent food allergy. *Allergy, Asthma & Clinical Immunology, 60*(4), 338-339.

33. Australasian Society of Clinical Immunology and Allergy. (2021). *Food Allergy.* ASCIA. Retrieved 2021, from https://www.allergy.org.au/patients/food-allergy.

34. Coulthard, H., Harris, G., & Emmett, P. (2009, Jan). Delayed introduction of lumpy foods to children during the complementary feeding period affects child's food acceptance and feeding at 7 years of age. *Matern Child Nutr, 5*(1), 75-85.

35. Australian Government: Department of Health. (2011, April). *Choking risks for toddlers and young children.* The Department of Health. Retrieved 2021, from https://www1.health.gov.au/internet/publications/publishing.nsf/Content/gug-director-toc~gug-foodsafety~gug-foodsafety-choking.

36. Maier, A., Chabanet, C., Schaal, B., Issanchou, S., & Leathwood, P. (2007, Dec). Effects of repeated exposure on acceptance of initially disliked vegetables in 7-month old infants. *Food Quality and Preference, 18*(8), 1023-1032.

37. Sullivan, S., & Birch, L. (1994, Feb). Infant dietary experience and acceptance of solid foods. *Pediatrics, 93*(2), 271-277.

38. Birch, L., & Marlin, D. (1982, Dec). I don't like it; I never tried it: effects of exposure on two-year-old children's food preferences. *Appetite, 3*(4), 353-360.

39. Birch, L., McPhee, L., Shoba, B., Pirok, E., & Steinberg, L. (1987, Dec). What kind of exposure reduces

children's food neophobia? Looking vs. tasting. *Appetite, 9*(3), 171-178

40. Sullivan, S., & Birch, L. (1990). Pass the sugar, pass the salt: Experience dictates preference. *Developmental Psychology, 26*(4), 546-551.

41. Lovell, A. 2019. *Fussy Eating in Children* [Webinar]. [Online].. Education In Nutrition. Available from: https://educationinnutrition.com.au/.

42. Cohen, R., Brown, K., Canahuati, J., Rivera, L., & Dewey, K. (1994, Jul). Effects of age of introduction of complementary foods on infant breast milk intake, total energy intake, and growth: a randomised intervention study in Honduras. *Lancet, 344*(8918), 288-293.

43. Daniels, L., Mallan, K., Battistutta, D., Nicholson, J., Perry, R., & Magarey, A. (2012, Oct). Evaluation of an intervention to promote protective infant feeding practices to prevent childhood obesity: outcomes of the NOURISH RCT at 14 months of age and 6 months post the first of two intervention modules. *Int J Obes (Lond), 36*(10), 1292-1298.

44. Galloway, A., Fiorito, L., Francis, L., & Birch, L. (2006, May). 'Finish your soup': counterproductive effects of pressuring children to eat on intake and affect. *Appetite, 46*(3), 318-323.

45. Griffiths, G., & Stapleton, D. (2013). *Sense-ational mealtimes! : making sense of tricky mealtime behaviour, fussy/picky eating and feeding difficulties.*

46. Canberra Hospital and Health Services. (2018). *Clinical Guideline: Feeding Guideline for Inafnts and Young Children.* ACT Government.

47. Raising Children Network. (n.d.). *Introducing solids: why, when, what and how.* Raising Children: The Australian Parenting Website. Retrieved 2021, from https://raisingchildren.net.au/babies/breastfeeding-bottle-feeding-solids/solids-drinks/introducing-solids.

48. Centre for Disease Control and Prevention. (2020, 11 9). *Nutrition: How Much and How Often to Feed.* Centre for Disease Control and Prevention. Retrieved 2021, from https://www.cdc.gov/nutrition/infantandtoddlernutrition/foods-and-drinks/how-much-and-how-often.html.

49. Food Standards Australia & New Zealand. (2020, Jan). *Arsenic in rice-based infant food products.*

Food Standards Australia & New Zealand. https://www.foodstandards.gov.au/consumer/chemi-cals/arsenic/Pages/default.aspx.

50. Zhang, T., Shi, Y., Zhao, Y., Tang, G., Niu, B., & Chen, Q. (2018, Sep). Boiling and roasting treatment affecting the peanut allergenicity. *Ann Transl Med*, 6(18), 357.

51. Food Standards Australia New Zealand. (n.d.). *Mercury in fish: Advice on fish consumption*. Food Standards Australia New Zealand.

52. AGENCY FOR CLINICAL INNOVATION. (2011). *Nutrition Standards for paediatric inpatients in NSW hospitals*. ACI Nutrition Network.

Made in the USA
Coppell, TX
02 July 2024

34181717R00077